ANIMAL ECOLOGY

W. H. Dowdeswell, M.A.
WINCHESTER COLLEGE

HARPER TORCHBOOKS ❦ THE SCIENCE LIBRARY

HARPER & BROTHERS, NEW YORK

To
the many young biologists who have contributed
unknowingly to the writing
of this book

Printed in the United States of America

This book was first published in 1952
by Methuen & Co., Ltd., London;
a second edition was issued in 1959,
which is here reprinted by arrangement.

First HARPER TORCHBOOK edition published 1961

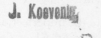

PREFACE

DURING the last twenty years or so, the study of ecology has made vast strides particularly in its application to the economic requirements of man. Such progress, coupled with a recently renewed interest in Natural History, has brought about wide-spread enthusiasm for the subject from the more academic standpoint, particularly in so far as elementary study by schools and first year University students is concerned. This tendency is reflected in the syllabus of many examinations.

There is no doubt that the study of ecology, if properly supervised, is of great value to the elementary biologist. In the first place it serves to bring him face to face with problems of adaptation and the distribution of animals and plants in nature, leading to a concept of the dynamic process of evolution. Furthermore, it provides an admirable means of training students in the use of the scientific method. No two animal habitats are exactly similar, either in their physical characteristics or in the nature of their resident fauna. Ecology thus constitutes the one branch of biology studied at an elementary level, in which problems can readily be subjected to inquiry, and to which 'the book' provides no absolute answer. Such studies, if carefully conducted, should thus prove both stimulating and instructive.

Of all biological subjects, ecology is one of the most difficult to teach on account of its apparent lack of precision, and the great number of variables operating under natural conditions. In consequence, it has become customary in some quarters to place the major emphasis on the taxonomic aspect of the subject, and largely to disregard the agencies concerned in bringing about spatial distribution. Admittedly it is seldom possible to determine these with accuracy, but none the less, the principal factors at work can generally be elucidated with patience and careful observation. Much of the aura of haziness which still tends to enshroud animal ecology is due to the imperfection of our present knowledge, a fact to be borne in mind when deciding the proportion of time to be allotted to its study in an elementary course of zoology. The science of biology is a discipline no less than physics or chemistry, and as our knowledge has grown, its treatment has inevitably become more precise and increasingly quantitative in approach. This trend is much in evidence to-day and undoubtedly represents one of the big advances in modern ecology. The estimation of animal populations and the fluctuations to which they are subject, also the detailed study of the influence of physical factors on distribution, are but two examples from a vast field of experimental work which has helped to convert the subject from a purely descriptive one into a branch of science.

The objects of this book are twofold: first to show what is meant by the animal's environment and the kind of results which environmental influences can achieve; second to determine the bearing of ecology on evolution. The field covered is thus a large one, and in order to restrict the pages to a reasonable number, emphasis has been laid throughout on ecological principles rather than detailed factual information. No attempt has been made to conform to the requirements of any particular examination syllabus, but it is my hope that this book may prove useful to General Certificate students at Advanced and Scholarship levels, University Scholarship candidates, and also during first year University zoology courses. An elementary knowledge of comparative anatomy and physiology is assumed, such as is normally acquired during the first and second years' school Sixth-Form work. Familiarity with the elements of genetics and the theory of evolution is also desirable, but not essential, for the understanding of the greater part of the text. The majority of the technical terms used are defined in the Glossary.

In order to illustrate points of ecological importance it has frequently been necessary to quote the names of animals and plants. Clearly it is impossible to provide pictures of all of these, and no doubt some will be unfamiliar to the reader. Wherever possible, all examples have been selected from the fauna and flora of Britain. On occasions where a principle is best illustrated by a foreign species, a British alternative has been given as well whenever practicable. In addition, an abbreviated Classification Table has been included which will enable animals to be placed in their correct class. An extensive Bibliography is also provided which contains a representative list of books covering the various aspects of ecology and natural history, in particular, the problem of identification.

It may be argued that any account of ecology should include an equal treatment of animals and plants. This is indeed true. But at the same time, it must be borne in mind that plant ecology has already been covered at all levels in numerous good books, as reference to the Bibliography will show. Publications dealing with general animal ecology are, however, relatively few, and many of them are unduly biased in one direction or another. A need therefore clearly exists for a broader treatment of the subject at an elementary level, and this has been my aim.

Although this book is therefore primarily concerned with animals, reference is constantly made throughout to their vital relationship with plants and the dependence of one upon the other. A list of suitable references to current works on plant ecology is included in the Bibliography.

While writing this book, I have received much encouragement from Dr. E. B. Ford, F.R.S., who has also read the typescript in detail. I should like to take this opportunity of thanking him for his criticism and many helpful suggestions. I also wish to thank Dr. M. Ashby for the trouble he has taken in preparing many of the diagrams, for reading the proofs, and for his kind advice on various other problems.

The following kindly provided photographs for reproduction: Mr. A. H. Bastin (Plate 3a); Mr. S. Beaufoy (Plates 2, 5, 6, 16); Mr. Eric Hosking (Plate 4); Veterinary Laboratory, Ministry of Agriculture and Fisheries (Plate 3b); and Mr. D. P. Wilson (Plates 9, 10, 12). I should like to express my thanks to them also to Dr. Finn Salomonsen for allowing me to reproduce Fig. 1. Professor L. A. Harvey has been most helpful in providing details of methods for determining various physical factors (pp. 172–5), as employed on his Summer Course of Field Studies. I have used all of these myself and found them well suited to classwork.

I am also grateful to Professor G. C. Varley, who kindly allowed me to borrow from the Hope Department of Entomology, Oxford, some of the insects figured in Plate 5, and to Mr. P. M. Sheppard, who supplied the snails shown in Plate 6 together with information relating to their genetics and the adaptive significance of their colours.

TIVERTON,

November 1950.

PREFACE TO SECOND EDITION

THE need for a second edition has enabled me to rewrite certain sections and to bring others up to date. The amount of alteration necessary has been influenced to a considerable extent by the recent publication of my *Practical Animal Ecology*. This covers somewhat similar ground but in more detail and with emphasis on the experimental aspects of the subject. The two books are, therefore, complementary, the former providing a theoretical background for the latter. At first sight, Chapter IX on "Practical Animal Ecology" would appear to be redundant, since its contents are repeated and greatly amplified in the more recent work. However, it has been retained nonetheless in the belief that there are some, particularly beginners, who will wish for a concise summary of essential practical techniques before proceeding to a more advanced approach.

Apart from adjustments to the text, three Figures have been redrawn (No. 2, 11, and 24). My grateful thanks are due to my colleague, Mr. W. M. M. Baron for preparing the new diagrams. The Bibliography has been considerably enlarged and brought up to date with the kind help of Mrs. J. H. Preston.

WINCHESTER   W. H. D.

January, 1959

CONTENTS

TEXT ILLUSTRATIONS

PLATES

CHAPTER I

ECOLOGY AND ITS BACKGROUND

THE ORIGIN OF ECOLOGY

ECOLOGY is a comparatively new term used to describe a very ancient branch of study. It was first coined in 1878 by the great German biologist Haeckel,[1] to denote the relationships of living organisms however near or distant, both with one another and with the physical environment in which they live.

Until the time of Haeckel, this branch of biology was known as Natural History. We may well ask then why it has been necessary to retain two terms both meaning much the same thing. The answer is not easy to give, as there exists no hard and fast distinction between them. In general, however, we may say that the need for a subdivision of the subject arose as a result of the vast increase in our knowledge of all branches of science during the nineteenth and twentieth centuries. The application of scientific methods and equipment to the solution of problems in natural history was inevitable, and resulted in a more technical and precise approach to the subject, and the beginning of ecology as we know it today.

Man's interest in natural history dates back to prehistoric times. The carvings and pictures of the early cave-dwellers in France and Spain, for instance, provide abundant evidence of their observation of the flora and fauna around them. Several of the early Roman and Greek writers interested themselves in the study of natural history, one of the most famous contributions being *The Histories of Animals* by Aristotle (384–322 B.C.). But the outstanding advances were made in the eighteenth and nineteenth centuries when the works of the great naturalists such as White's *Natural History of Selborne*, Darwin's *Naturalist's Voyage Round the World*, Wallace's *Island Life*, Bates's *Naturalist on*

[1] Derived from the Greek words οἶκος—house; λόγος—discourse.

the Amazons, and many others, added immeasurably to our biological knowledge. Any student of ecology would be well advised to read some of these works not only for their scientific worth, but also as admirable examples of careful observation and detailed description of animals and plants under natural conditions.

THE AIMS OF ECOLOGY

Ecology today represents the logical step forward from natural history once our scientific knowledge had reached a sufficiently advanced state. It is important therefore to understand not only the methods used in its study, but also the scope of the subject, which is constantly widening.

In the first place, ecology involves the application of the 'Scientific Method' to the study of organisms under natural conditions. By this is meant the logical analysis of a series of observations which will normally take place as follows:

>Phase I.   (*a*) Observation,
>   (*b*) Description.
>Phase II. (*a*) Analysis or sorting out of data,
>   (*b*) Conclusions.

Now the Old Naturalist was concerned largely with Phase I. His contributions often involved great patience, much detailed observation, and accurate description. But his conclusions, although extensive, were frequently incomplete and often lacked a quantitative and scientific background. The New Naturalist (ecologist) obtains his information by means often similar to the old, but seeks to employ wherever possible techniques from which the maximum of scientifically sound conclusions can be drawn.

Today, the difference between ecology and natural history is (or should be) merely one of degree, the former being a more advanced and technical version of the latter. Any further attempt here to segregate the two would serve no useful purpose, for no matter what criteria we adopt the one inevitably grades into the other.

THE SCOPE OF ECOLOGY

Ecology covers a vast biological field, and the solution of a particular problem may require several different lines of approach. None of these constitutes an end in itself, but each makes a small though important contribution to the complete picture.

These various aspects can be classified as:

(a) biotic,
(b) quantitative,
(c) climatic (physical and chemical),
(d) taxonomic,
(e) evolutionary and genetic.

Biotic factors are those which are the direct outcome of the activities of the animals themselves. We shall be concerned particularly with the problem of living space and its partition among the large number of competitors to be found in any community, also food supply in which plants play a vital role.

Quantitative study involves the estimation of numbers in different communities, and an assessment of population density in a given area. Information of this kind is often of value in solving problems of, say, food availability or movement within a particular colony.

Climatic factors include temperature, light, and humidity, also such important items as salinity and acidity in aquatic habitats. Some animals are remarkably sensitive to minute changes in their surroundings, and small climatic variations undoubtedly play a large part in determining distribution.

Taxonomy, the description, classification, and naming of organisms, is in some ways the most laborious and highly specialized part of biology. Although not an end in itself, it none the less forms the foundation of all ecological studies. During the early part of the present century the so-called Ecological Survey made its appearance. This all too often consisted merely in the naming of a large number of animals

and plants inhabiting a particular area, without consideration
of the circumstances enabling them to live there. Such a
tendency unfortunately still exists in some quarters today, and
it must be emphasized that these surveys only constitute one
aspect of ecology. Their results are thus of limited value unless
followed up by complementary observations of the various
ecological factors concerned.

The evolutionary and genetic aspects of ecology have increased in importance during recent years as our knowledge of
heredity and the mechanism of Natural Selection has advanced.
There is often a tendency, particularly among junior students,
to regard evolution as a thing of the past, and to overlook the
fact that it is a dynamic process at work all the time. By its
very nature, its progress is generally slow. In certain circumstances however, it is possible to detect and even measure its
rate of action in wild populations (see pp. 26–9).

These five subdivisions can be said to form the backbone of
ecology. An example will serve to show the kind of way in
which they may be related. Suppose we were asked to
study the ecology of a species of edible fish inhabiting a large
lake, with the object of enabling a new colony to be started
elsewhere. One of the first things we would have to discover
would be its food, and whether the species is itself the prey of
any other animals (predators) in the locality. Again it would
be desirable to know the number of individuals that could live
successfully in a given area without overcrowding. These are
biotic factors, the last of which leads us to a consideration of
numbers, and an estimate of the size of the population in that
particular habitat. Here then is the quantitative aspect. We
should also have to study the water itself and fluctuations in its
constitution, such as salt content, acidity or alkalinity, in order
to determine the animal's tolerance of changing climatic
factors. If the lake were a very old one and the fish had been
isolated there for a great period of time, it is possible that a local
race or sub-species might have evolved. This is where the
experience of the taxonomist could help with identification.
Such a situation might lead us on to consider the more

academic question of how and at what rate the new form could have evolved.

Finally, it might happen that two closely related species interbred when associated together in the same locality, as they do in the trout. A knowledge of the genetics involved would then be of value in finding a form best suited to withstand the particular conditions in the new locality.

ANIMAL HABITATS

There is hardly a place on the earth's surface that cannot be colonized by some animal. Different species are sometimes able to adapt themselves to the most unlikely conditions such as the nematode worms which inhabit vinegar vats, butterflies which fly among snow-clad mountain peaks, and fishes which live for considerable periods in mud baked solid by the sun. Even the members of a single species may live in widely differing circumstances in areas not far distant from one another. It is only possible here to analyse the factors affecting animal colonization in a general way. For this purpose the four commonest types of habitat will be considered, namely:

(a) terrestrial,
(b) marine,
(c) estuarine,
(d) fresh water.

Each of these is characterized by certain ecological features which permit colonization by its own peculiar fauna.

SYNECOLOGY AND AUTECOLOGY

During recent years there has been a growing tendency to consider ecology under two distinct headings, namely *synecology* and *autecology*. The distinction is purely an arbitrary one, and since it will not be referred to again, a brief explanation is necessary. Synecology applies to circumstances in which the plants and animals of a particular locality are regarded as comprising an organic whole or single ecological unit. Such a concept can be expanded or contracted at will to embrace any area from a continent to a small pool. Autecology on the other hand assumes as its basis not the community, but the species, and involves the study of its relationship with the environment; that is to say the various ecological factors determining its distribution. It will be seen that sooner or later any study of synecology is bound to grade into autecology and vice versa. The problems considered here are largely those of synecology.

THE GEOLOGICAL BASIS OF ECOLOGY

The following chapters deal almost entirely with the ecology of Britain as it is *today*. It is important to realize, however, that the physical environment in which animals live is not static but is constantly changing. Such changes are sometimes great and rapid but more often small and slow. The majority are natural and result from climatic factors of various kinds, but nowadays the influence of man is playing an ever greater part in producing them. As their surroundings change so do the organisms themselves, the process being known as *evolution*. This has resulted in the plant and animal communities as we know them. When studying these, it is desirable to have some idea of the way in which they arose, for this frequently provides important information for the solution of certain kinds of ecological problems.

The only direct evidence that evolution has occurred in the past is to be found in the rocks and the petrified remains of former plants and animals (fossils) which they sometimes contain.

The term 'rock', as used by the geologist, covers all constituents of the earth's surface except the actual soil. These may be of many kinds, ranging from a hard impermeable layer such as granite to a soft porous medium like sandstone. They may be formed in two distinct ways. The first consists in the slow deposition of successive layers of material such as the sediment of flowing rivers, the progressive decay of plants, or the washing up of sand by the sea. These layers (strata) become compressed and sometimes subject to various chemical changes, the result being *stratified rocks*. Another kind of rock formation results from volcanic eruption and the solidification of molten lava which gives rise to *igneous rocks*. Reference to the Geological Survey of some parts of Britain will show that two distinct maps exist covering the same area. One of these shows the 'solid' geology, that is to say the old stratified rocks, but omits the superficial deposits such as glacial sands and gravels. The other records the 'drift' geology, and includes only the recent surface deposits. While drift geology is of great importance to the biologist in the study of present-day soils and the vegetation which they can support, solid geology is equally vital to the palaeontologist; for within the layers of the old stratified rocks the fossilized remains of many animals and plants are often preserved with much of their original detail still intact. It is thus possible to arrange the different strata according to a geological sequence, each being characterized by its own peculiar fossil flora and fauna which existed at the time of its deposition (see Table I, pp. 8–9).

The analysis of radio-active minerals has enabled geologists to form an approximate idea of the duration of the various periods of sedimentation, so that we can now think in terms not only of geological space, but also of time as well. In describing a rock layer, the term *System* is used to denote the largest entity. This is subdivided into a number of *Formations*. Similarly, the main divisions of geological time are known as *Eras*, each including a number of *Periods* (or *Epochs*). These are summarized in Table I, together with their approximate duration in millions of years, and the characteristic flora and fauna associated with them.

THE PLEISTOCENE IN BRITAIN

From an ecological point of view the most important part of geological history in Britain was the Pleistocene period (see Table I) for it was then, and during the few thousand years

TABLE I

Simplified Geological Time Scale (British deposits)

Eras (figures represent approx. duration in millions of years)	Periods	Systems and formations found in Britain	Predominant animals and plants
Holocene (Recent)	(1/40)	Alluvium, Peat, Silt, Marshland	
Tertiary (Cenozoic) 70	Upper (15)	*Pleistocene* Glacial Drifts, Boulder Clay (4 separate Ice-Ages)	
		Pliocene Norwich and Red Crag	Man (at first, several species)
	Middle (20)	*Miocene* Not found in Britain	
	Lower (35)	*Oligocene* Hampstead and Headon Beds	
		Eocene Bagshot Sands, London Clay	Placentals
	Cretaceous (55)	Chalk (Downs and Wolds); Greensand and Gault; Weald Clay; Hastings Sands	True flowering plants

Era	Period	Rock formations	Life forms
Secondary (Mesozoic) 125	Jurassic (30)	Purbeck beds; Portland beds; Oxford Clay; Bath Oolite Series; Lias Clay (Lyme Regis)	Birds
	Triassic (40)	New Red Marls; New Red Sandstone	Mammals
	Permian (30)	Magnesian Limestone and Marls (Vale of York)	Reptiles
Primary (Palaeozoic) 310	Carboniferous (60)	Coal Measures; Millstone Grit (Bristol, Yorks.); Mountain Limestone (Pennines, Mendips)	Amphibians
	Devonian (40)	Old Red Sandstone (Wales, Scotland); Grey Slates (Devon and Cornwall)	Insects, Trees and Seed plants
	Silurian (30)	Ludlow and Wenlock Shales	Fishes
	Ordovician (50)	Bala and Skiddaw Slates, etc.	
	Cambrian (100)	Harlech Grits & Slates, etc.	
Pre-Cambrian (extent unknown 2845 +)		Torridonian Sandstone, Granite, Schists, Gneiss, Igneous	Invertebrates

immediately afterwards, that the nature of our present-day fauna was determined. It is interesting to find that some of the genera and species generally regarded as comprising the Pleistocene fauna still exist here to-day. For this reason it is worth while examining the sequence of events during that time in some detail.

To begin with it should be realized that no two authorities agree on this subject, which is hardly surprising in view of the great lapse of time involved and the scanty evidence often available. However, the main happenings during that period are now sufficiently understood to make possible a brief and rather generalized summary of them. The following account is based largely on the analysis by Boswell recently summarized by Stamp.

The end of the Pliocene in Britain was characterized by a climate very similar to that of the present day. The land was populated by plants closely resembling those occurring now, while such animals as the Straight-Tusked Elephant (*Elephas antiquus*), the Hippopotamus, and Rhinoceros (*R. merckii*) were still in evidence. The sea water was much colder than at present and colonized by an arctic or sub-arctic fauna, the molluscs being predominant.

The Pleistocene which followed (see Table II) consisted of four glacial periods with three interglacials between them. The First Glacial spread from the high ground of Scandinavia across the North Sea to the coast of Durham and Yorkshire and the low ground of eastern Norfolk. Many of the higher parts of the country must have been snow-bound. It is possible that man inhabiting Britain at this time was of the Piltdown type (*Eoanthropus*). The retreat of the ice and melting of the snow marked the First Interglacial with a relatively warm climate lasting many thousands of years. The implements made by man during this interval were of the Chellean type being rather rough and crude.

The First Interglacial ended with the gradual onset of colder conditions, resulting in the formation of extensive glaciers mainly in the eastern part of the country. During this Second

Glaciation, Chalk Boulder Clay was deposited. This was followed by the Second Interglacial and a period of warmer conditions. The country was inhabited by a rich fauna and flora, the implements made by man being of the Acheulian type and showing a great advance over those of the Chellean culture. Since these are absent from the north of England, we may conclude that conditions there were still too cold for human habitation. This is believed to have been the longest of the interglacials, and towards its close Neanderthal Man (*Homo neanderthalensis*), who was the maker of Mousterian implements, made his appearance.

A fresh advance of the ice southwards marked the beginning of the Third Glacial, during which time the cold conditions were more universal in the north and extended southwards as far as the Thames. Remains of the Mammoth (*Elephas primigenius*) are to be found in the deposits belonging to this period. The Third Interglacial which followed was characterized by the appearance of Modern Man (*Homo sapiens*) with his beautifully fashioned implements of the Aurignacian type. It was of shorter duration and cooler than the Second, and was followed by the Fourth Glaciation which was much less intense than the Third, although great glaciers were formed on the high ground of the Lake District and elsewhere. Sub-arctic or tundra conditions prevailed over much of the country. The animals characteristic of them were the Reindeer, Arctic Fox, and Marmot. By this time, those typical of an arctic climate such as the Mammoth had disappeared, although isolated colonies of animals and plants of the Interglacial type still survived in the west (even in Scotland), and in Ireland. It is at present impossible to give a precise estimate of the duration of these various Pleistocene Ages. Suffice it to say that they must have occupied tens of thousands of years.

With the end of the last Pleistocene Ice Age, we pass into Holocene times with the Magdalenian culture of man. This phase has been dated to approximately 8300 B.C., and was characterized by a dry, cold Pre-boreal or Sub-arctic climate lasting about 1500 years. This was succeeded about 6800 B.C.

TABLE II

Summary of Events in Britain During and After the Pleistocene

	Climatic conditions	Human remains and cultures	Characteristic fauna and flora
Post-Glacial (HOLOCENE)	Sub-Atlantic Age. 'Oceanic' climate characteristic of Britain today. About 1000 B.C.	Historic times	Similar to that existing at the present day
	Atlantic age. Wetter and warmer than today. About 5000 B.C. Connection between England and Continent severed		
	Boreal age. 'Continental' climate. Dry, with cold winters and warm summers. About 6800 B.C.		Appearance of oak and other deciduous trees
	Pre-boreal (Sub-arctic) conditions. Dry and cold. Duration about 1500 years	Neolithic (New Stone Age) Polished instruments	Pine, birch and willow, predominant trees
Fourth Glacial	Less intense than Third glaciation but cold in North. Tundra conditions over most of Britain. Ended about 8300 B.C.	Magdalenian culture	Reindeer, Arctic Fox, Marmot. Mammoth and most other arctic animals extinct

Period	Conditions	Man / Culture	Fauna
Third Interglacial	Shorter and cooler than Second Interglacial	Modern man (*Homo sapiens*) Aurignacian culture	
Third Glacial	Cold conditions as far south as Thames	Mousterian culture	Mammoth
Second Interglacial	Longest Interglacial. Relatively warm in the South but cold in the North	Swanscombe Man (*Homo sapiens?*) Acheulian culture of Neanderthal Man (*Homo neanderthalensis*)	Rich fauna and flora in South
Second Glacial	Great glaciation, particularly in the East of England	Chellean culture	
First Interglacial	Relatively warm period lasting many thousands of years		Straight-tusked Elephant still in evidence
First Glacial (PLEISTOCENE)	Ice sheet from Scandinavia to coast of Durham and Yorkshire		
Pre-Glacial (PLIOCENE)	Sub-Atlantic conditions. Similar to the present day but sea much colder		Straight-tusked Elephant, Hippopotamus and Rhinoceros. Molluscs predominant in the sea

by a Boreal Age with a climate of the 'continental' type with cold winters and warm summers. The dominant trees which had previously been pine, birch, and willow, were gradually augmented by oak and other deciduous species. About 5000 B.C. the connection between England and the Continent finally disappeared, the succeeding 'Atlantic Age' being wet and warmer than to-day. The Sub-Atlantic conditions with an Oceanic climate characteristic of Britain at present can be dated from about 1000 B.C.

BRITAIN AS AN ECOLOGICAL UNIT

The foregoing account shows that, apart from present-day migrants, the modern fauna of Britain must have been derived from two sources:

(i) Glacial forms and those which reached the country during or prior to the last Ice Age.

(ii) Post-glacial colonists from the Continent which arrived as a result of a northward movement during the period of about 4000 years, which intervened between the final recession of the ice and the disappearance of the land connection with England in 6000–5000 B.C.

The survivors of the Ice Age such as the Pigmy Shrew (*Sorex minutus*), often referred to as Ice Age relicts, although comparatively few in number, provide important ecological evidence, the significance of which will be discussed later (see p. 24).

The post-glacial colonists from the east and south-east were faced with a race against time. Many species, on arrival in England, found their passage to Ireland already blocked by the Irish Channel. This accounts for the absence of snakes from Ireland which, although attributed to St. Patrick, was in fact due to their isolation in Britain. Among our mammals, the Brown Hare (*Lepus europaeus*), Mole (*Talpa europaea*), Roe Deer (*Cervus capreolus*), Water Vole (*Arvicola amphibius*), and Great Bat or Noctule (*Nyctalus noctula*) to mention only a few, are all absentees from Ireland.

A similar situation occurred as a result of the formation of the English Channel, animals with a slower rate of spread from the east finding their passage northwards barred by the sea. Thus a comparison of the fauna of Britain and the Continent shows us to be the poorer in almost every respect. Among mammals for instance, 58 species are found on the Continent of which only 43 occur in Britain. Of these, only about 25 are found in Ireland. This poverty in our fauna extends not only to mammals, but to other vertebrates and invertebrates as well.

To-day, the majority of the animals in Britain are completely isolated from neighbouring land and thus present a compact ecological picture. Furthermore, having been cut off fairly recently, we are able to compare them with their continental relatives, and so follow the course of their evolution and the influence of isolation upon it.

CHAPTER II

THE DISTRIBUTION OF ANIMALS

THE CHANGING ENVIRONMENT

IN order to survive successfully, plants and animals must be well adapted to the circumstances in which they live. In Chapter I we saw how their *environment*, as it is generally known, is in a constant state of flux on account of changes in the various ecological factors concerned. Such changes are usually slow. During the Pleistocene era for instance, the four glacial periods were followed successively by intervals of comparative warmth, each with a duration of tens of thousands of years (see Table II). These variations in climate gradually exerted their influence on the animal and plant communities which proceeded to evolve at different rates in the various parts of the world. During the last 2000 years man has played an ever-increasing role in upsetting the natural ecological balance. By his cultivation of the land, cutting down of timber, pollution of rivers, and construction of towns, to mention only a few instances, he is bringing about great changes in former animal and plant habitats. Some organisms are capable of becoming adapted to such alterations, others are not.

The survivors have frequently acquired new habits and modes of life, while extinction or severe restriction of range has been the fate of those that failed to do so. An animal which has thrived in the new circumstances is the House Sparrow (*Passer domesticus*). During medieval times it was comparatively rare in this country, but with the advances in building and the great increase in man's communal life during subsequent centuries, its habits have changed and it has become associated, more and more, with human dwelling places where its colonization has been a conspicuous success. It is now one of our commoner passerine birds. In America, too, it has multiplied from rarity to become a universal pest in less than a century.

1. BARRIERS TO THE MOVEMENT OF BUTTERFLIES (TEAN. ISLES OF SCILLY)

The area of bracken and long grass (to the right) almost prohibited the passage of the Common Blue (*Polyommatus icarus*), while the short grass (to the left) was a barrier to the Meadow Brown (*Maniola jurtina*)

(*a*) Normal form against natural background

(*b*) Melanic form against natural background

2. THE PEPPERED MOTH (*Biston betularia*)

On the other hand, a species that has suffered from man's activities is the Large Copper (*Lycaena dispar*), formerly the finest of our butterflies. Its range was confined to the Fens where the food plant of the larva was the Great Water Dock (*Rumex hydrolapathum*). The butterfly made its last appearance in this country in about 1848. Over-enthusiastic collecting by entomologists was probably the primary cause of extinction, although there were other secondary factors involved, the chief being the drainage of the Fens by man.

THE ENVIRONMENT AND COLONIZATION

The success of animal and plant species in inhabiting a particular locality is not all a matter of luck, although chance no doubt plays a considerable part in providing the initial opportunities for colonization. The distribution of organisms over the earth's surface is ultimately dependent on two main factors:

(i) *Movement,* enabling them to reach the locality in the first place. This may be achieved naturally by their own efforts, or with the help of some other agency such as the wind.

(ii) The *adaptability* of the species once it has reached the new area.

MOVEMENT AND COLONIZATION

Some form of movement either active or passive is essential if dispersal is to be achieved and the range thus increased. In plants this process is mainly passive, occurring during a resting stage in the life-cycle as a fruit, seed, or spore. In animals the reverse is true, and it is the adult which is largely responsible for dispersal. Exceptions are some static or slowly-moving aquatic forms where a larva or other special mobile phase fulfils this function, such as the medusa of coelenterates (e.g. *Obelia*). From the point of view of colonization, the efficiency of movement must be judged by the animal's ability to cross or circumvent obstacles. These may be of many kinds ranging from an expanse of sea to a small ditch, and in ecology are termed *barriers*. They are not always topographic, but may be climatic or even biotic. In Plate 1 (at p. 16) are shown two barriers occurring on Tean, Isles of Scilly, which play an important part in influencing the movement of butterflies. The area of bracken and long grass in the foreground was found almost to prohibit the passage of the Common Blue (*Polyommatus icarus*), whose distribution was confined to the exposed regions of short grass (in the background), which contained the food plants of the larva (various Leguminosae). This grassy zone proved a barrier to the Meadow Brown (*Maniola jurtina*) which was invariably found among the bracken, partly, no doubt, on account of the presence of its food plants (various grasses such as *Poa pratensis*), and partly due to its reluctance to fly across the windswept areas.

ADAPTABILITY AND COLONIZATION

Once an organism has reached a possible new habitat, the next task confronting it is to adapt itself to existing conditions in the face of competition from the other inhabitants. Some animals such as nematode worms show remarkable powers of adjustment and seem to be able to exist almost anywhere. Others are much more specific in their requirements, an extreme instance being the flatworms (Cestoda) which inhabit the alimentary canals of many animals and are unable to exist outside them.

The adaptive power of animals and plants is the direct outcome of the flexibility of their constitution. The more variable a species may be, so the greater the chance it has of evolving a form well suited to a certain set of conditions. Now the appearance of an organism (generally known as its *phenotype*) is the result of two distinct factors which react with one another, namely the external environment and its hereditary constitution (*gene-complex*). Changes in either of these may bring about corresponding alterations in the resulting individual. These responses of the gene-complex of the organism to the environment have to be made anew at every generation, and while the result may be favourable in one set of circumstances, it may be disadvantageous in another. Such *environmental* variation occurs irrespective of any alterations in the genetic factors (*genes*) themselves. An example will make this clear. In the shrimp-like crustacean *Gammarus chevreuxi*, the normal colour of the eyes is black due to the formation of a pigment, melanin, in the facets. Occasionally, however, red-eyed forms are found in which the melanin is absent. Now it has been shown that the genes which control these colours exert a physiological influence by affecting the rate at which melanin deposition occurs. Thus it is found that in the maternal brood pouch where early development takes place (the animal being viviparous), the eyes of the normal wild type are red like those which retain that coloration as adults. Subsequently, the production of melanin occurs in a few hours if the animal is destined to have black eyes, otherwise a trace only has been deposited after some months. Environmental conditions such as temperature and food influence this process. For example, in a genetically red-eyed form, rapid melanin formation can be induced at 28° C., the eyes becoming approximately black in twenty days. On the other hand, at 13° C., it is possible to arrest considerably the production of pigment in normal black-eyed individuals, the eyes remaining reddish for some months. The significance of this is not known, but it serves as an instance of the way in which changes in the environment may influence the variability of an organism. This is one means by which variation must frequently take place under wild conditions.

Another kind of variation may occur which is independent of the environment and is known as *genetic*. This is due partly to sudden and unpredictable though very rare changes in the nature of genes (*mutations*), but predominantly to the immense possibilities of reassortment possessed by the genetic factors as a result of Mendelian (particulate) inheritance in organisms which reproduce sexually. This is primarily a matter for the geneticist and need not be discussed further here. Suffice it to say in conclusion that all plants and animals exhibit variation to some degree, due to the mechanisms outlined above (see Bibliography for further references).

Under wild conditions subject to the influence of Natural Selection, those animals possessing beneficial variations will tend to survive and breed, while those less well suited to their surroundings will become scarce and eventually perish. Selection also takes place among the genes themselves. Thus in the heterozygote their effects become magnified (or mitigated), depending on whether they are advantageous or not in the particular circumstances. In this way dominance and recessiveness results.

ISOLATION IN ANIMAL COMMUNITIES

Animals often fail to colonize new areas, either because they cannot reach them, or because once there they are unable to become adapted to the new conditions. Furthermore, it sometimes happens that an animal which has once enjoyed a wide distribution becomes restricted to a number of smaller areas throughout its former range, giving a kind of mosaic effect on the ground. This is often a prelude to total extinction. The inevitable result of such failure to survive is *isolation*, i.e. the restriction of range to a well-defined region bounded by ecological barriers. This may happen in a number of different ways.

GEOGRAPHICAL ISOLATION

One of the commonest forms of isolation is *geographical*. This occurs when islands are formed from larger land masses, when river courses are altered either naturally or artificially, and as a result of the formation of mountain ranges and the isolation of lakes. Such barriers may be classed as physiographic, and they serve to mark off an area as a distinct geographical unit. Environmental conditions in these isolated places may change over a period of time and become significantly different from those which once prevailed, and to which the animal inhabitants were originally adapted. In this way, important ecological differences sometimes come to exist between the isolated and parent localities. Such changes are not only climatic but often biotic as well. For instance, they may result from the absence of former predators or the appearance of new ones, also from variations in the plants on which the animals are ultimately dependent. The process of

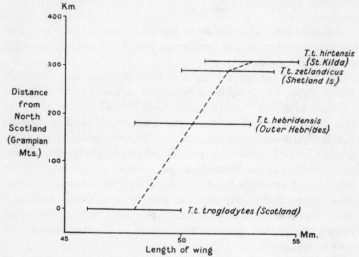

Fig. 1.—The influence of isolation on the size of four sub-species of the Wren (*Troglodytes troglodytes*).

(After Salomonsen)

isolation results eventually in the formation of geographical races which in the course of time may evolve into sub-species or even species. The stage at which one is deemed to have changed into the other is to some extent arbitrary, and a matter for the systematist to decide. Several well-known instances occur in Britain, such as the Wren (*Troglodytes troglodytes*). This forms distinct sub-species on St. Kilda, the Shetlands, and other Outer Hebridean islands. The St. Kilda Wren (*T. t. hirtensis*) is more greyish-brown above with paler under-parts than the normal form, the barring being heavier and more extensive on the mantle. The Shetland race (*T. t. zetlandicus*) differs from

the normal in being darker and more bulky in appearance.
The Hebridean Wren (*T. t. hebridensis*) is similar to the Shetland, but the under-parts are more buff in colour and the
barring not so heavy. There are also marked differences in
the size of the various forms (see Fig. 1).

SEASONAL ISOLATION

Another kind of isolation is *seasonal*. This may result when
variation occurs in the breeding time of the individuals of a
particular species.

Its causes are unknown, but the situation has probably
arisen from the combined action of a number of different
agencies of which climate and availability of food are no doubt
the chief. Thus in Britain, the Common Marbled Carpet
Moth (*Dysstroma truncata*) has two broods, while the closely
related Dark Marbled Carpet (*D. citrata*) has only one. These
two species can be induced to pair under experimental conditions and produce fertile offspring intermediate in appearance between the two parents. But in nature this seldom if
ever happens because the adults of *citrata* are on the wing
during the period between the broods of *truncata*, and so the
two do not meet.

ECOLOGICAL ISOLATION

Even in quite a small locality, the influence of the various
ecological factors on the range of an animal species may vary
considerably in different places. The result will be *ecological*
isolation and a consequent discontinuous distribution. This
has probably happened in the Sand Lizard (*Lacerta agilis*)
which mainly inhabits isolated localities in Dorset, Hants, and
Surrey. It is found only on sandy heathland, and no doubt
both climatic and biotic factors have contributed to restrict its
range to this small area.

A special instance of ecological isolation is that resulting
from variations in *altitude* within the range of a species. The
factors concerned are often difficult to unravel with any

certainty, but temperature and wind are two of the most important. In Britain, one of the most striking examples of this kind
is provided by our only Alpine butterfly, the Mountain Ringlet
(*Erebia epiphron*). In England, this is confined to the mountains
of the Lake District where it is not found below 1800 feet. In
Scotland its distribution is wider and in the mountainous
areas of Perth and Inverness its habitat extends as low as 1500
feet. Thus altitude requirements in this species have produced
two isolated and quite distinct races.

But the commonest cause of ecological isolation is undoubtedly the presence or absence of suitable food. In extreme
instances, this may cause a species to inhabit a single area only,
but more often the result is a discontinuous distribution, as in
the Colorado Beetle (*Leptinotarsa decemlineata*) whose original
home was in the Rocky Mountains of North America. Here its
range was restricted by the occurrence of its food plant the
Buffalo Bur (*Solanum rostratum*). The introduction of the
potato by man, also other suitable alternative foods such as
the tobacco plant, promoted its wide and rapid spread in the
United States. Climatic factors appear to have had little
controlling influence on this insect, since it has proved itself
able to withstand great variations in temperature and humidity. It was accidentally introduced into France in 1922,
where it has now become a universal potato pest throughout
the greater part of the country. Its first outbreak in England
was discovered in 1933, and although it has not managed to
establish itself here in any numbers, it none the less constitutes a potential menace to potato cultivation throughout
much of Western Europe.

ISOLATION OF RELICT FAUNAS

Mention has already been made (p. 14) of the peculiar
conditions which confronted the indigenous animals of Britain
at the end of the last Pleistocene Ice Age. The northern ice
sheet was gradually retreating towards the Arctic and the
southern one towards the Alps, leaving behind them a

post-glacial zone with a climate becoming steadily warmer. Many species had managed to survive the glacial conditions, and these 'relicts' as they are called, were now faced with the task of becoming adapted to considerable changes in temperature. Those with a wide temperature tolerance (*eurythermous*) were able to do so to varying extents, while the *stenothermous* forms (adapted to a narrow temperature range) tended either to follow the retreating ice caps, or to become extinct. Two of our best-known relict species are to be found among the freshwater flatworms (Turbellaria), *Planaria alpina* and *Polycelis*

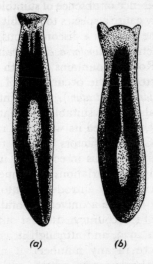

(a)   *(b)*

Fig. 2.—Two Turbellarian Ice Age Relicts. (a) *Planaria alpina* (b) *Polycelis cornuta* (×6 approx.)

cornuta (see Fig. 2). While exterminated in the larger watercourses which they no doubt inhabited at the time of the retreating ice, they have survived as small colonies in isolated areas of cold water arising from mountain springs. Similarly among fishes, the genus *Coregonus* of the Salmon family (Salmonidae) is found in many lakes formed by the post-glacial shrinkage of the great European rivers. Once isolated, each community has evolved independently, with the result that in Britain and Switzerland to-day, each lake basin is found to have its own particular species or sub-species of salmon.

ISOLATION AND VARIABILITY

When a number of individuals belonging to a common species are examined, it is often surprising how constant in appearance they seem to be. In a small island such as England, an animal appears more often than not to possess a single form throughout its range provided its distribution is fairly continuous. This is due to the selection of that combination of genes in the organism which reacts most favourably with an external environment which is virtually constant.

When variation occurs in such forms, it is not always discontinuous as one might expect if isolation were responsible for it. Some species are more sensitive to environmental change than others and often succeed in becoming adapted to differing extents in the various parts of their range. We have seen how complete isolation tends to produce distinct geographical races and eventually new species. But isolation is often incomplete and results in a kind of gradient of variability throughout the inhabited zone. This is known as a *cline* and may be due to ecological or geographical causes. The principle is well illustrated by the Coal Tit (*Parus ater*) which exhibits three distinct clines in western Europe. The most obvious of these is an increase in the yellow colouring of the feathers, and runs from east to west. Thus in the three sub-species of this bird, *P. a. ater* from the Continent, *P. a. britannicus* from Britain, and *P. a. hibernicus* from Ireland, the white parts of the plumage tend to become progressively tinged with yellow and the grey parts more olive-buff as the range extends westwards. As might be expected, Irish specimens may overlap the British form, but this only occurs in eastern Ireland. A somewhat similar situation occurs in Wales, the cline thus continuing as if the Irish Channel were not there. The differences in appearance between the members of two populations separated by a formidable barrier such as an expanse of sea, are likely to be greater than those between the various colonies of a species within whose range there is no such interruption and where distribution is more or less continuous. This is true in the Coal Tit. The significance of this particular cline is not known, but sometimes such variation may be a great advantage to an animal as in the mouse *Peromyscus polionotus*. In Florida three sub-species occur, namely *P. p. leucocephalus*, an almost white form, *P. p. polionotus*, the normal dark type, and *P. p. albifrons*, which is pale in colour and intermediate between the other two. These exhibit a gradient in pigmentation directly related to changes in the colour of the surroundings in which the animals live. *P. p. leucocephalus*, being an island form and living on white sand, shows no tendency to vary throughout its range. *P. p. albifrons* occupies a similar habitat, but on the shore of the mainland, and shows a pronounced tendency to darkening farther inland. The region of overlap between the pale *P. p. albifrons* and the dark inland form *P. p. polionotus* about forty miles from the coast, is only a few miles wide, *P. p. polionotus* thereafter becoming invariable and matching the darker background prevailing throughout its range. This abrupt change from one sub-species to the other is just what we would expect, for the effects of Natural Selection will be most intense in an area where neither is adapted to match its surroundings.

The study of clines is of comparatively recent origin and our knowledge of them is at present small, largely owing to the laborious enquiries necessary to establish their existence. There is every reason to believe that they are far more widespread than present evidence suggests.

RATES OF ADAPTATION IN WILD POPULATIONS

Evolution under natural conditions is generally a slow process although in certain circumstances it may be greatly accelerated. The rate at which an animal can evolve and adapt itself to changing conditions must play a large part in determining the success of its competition with other organisms, and hence the extent of its distribution. Many species have been evolving for millions of years, and it is necessary to turn to the fossil-bearing rocks for evidence of the various stages

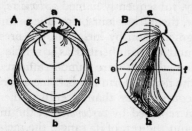

Fig. 3.—A typical Brachiopod (*Terebratula*) from the Upper Chalk to show the arrangement of the shells. · × ⅔.
(*A*) Dorsal view; (*B*) lateral view. (*a*) posterior; (*b*) anterior; (*a–b*) length; (*c–d*) width; (*e–f*) thickness; (*g–h*) hinge line.

(*From Woods*)

involved. An extreme example of slow evolution is provided by the Brachiopoda or Lamp Shells (see Fig. 3) of which the genus *Crania* occurs commonly in shallow water off the west coast of Ireland. These animals attained their zenith during Palaeozoic times and with the exception of one genus (*Lingula*), which is not found in British waters, have declined in numbers ever since. One of the most remarkable features of *Crania* is that specimens found in the earliest fossil-bearing rocks closely resemble those existing at the present day. In other words, the animal has hardly evolved at all over a period of approximately five hundred million years!

The process of evolution is generally much more rapid than this. For instance, the marsupial mammals in Australia evolved from small primitive creatures during the Cretaceous period to their present-day highly specialized condition in about fifty million years.

On rare occasions adaptation may proceed at a great rate

when suitable conditions arise, generally as a result of man's activities. This has happened in the Peppered Moth (*Biston betularia*) inhabiting the industrial areas of northern England (see Plate 2, at p. 17). Before 1850 the only form known in this region was the normal pale-coloured one. But during that year a black variety, subsequently named *carbonaria*, was first found in Manchester, the dark colour being due to an increase in the amount of pigmentation by melanin. On breeding, the condition was found to be inherited as a simple dominant. By about 1910 the two forms were found in almost equal numbers, while to-day the normal form has become a rare variety in this area. In the course of less than a century, therefore, the wild form has been replaced by *carbonaria* in the industrial north, while throughout the rest of its range, the melanic insect now remains a rarity only in the most rural districts. This must be one of the most remarkable instances of rapid evolution ever witnessed, and man has undoubtedly been responsible for bringing it about. In the heavily industrialized areas the large quantities of soot liberated into the air daily, pollute the vegetation. Kettlewell has recently demonstrated that under these conditions the black form is at an advantage over its normal counterpart, being better concealed from predatory birds such as the hedge sparrow, spotted fly-catcher and nut-hatch. The reason why predation had never previously been observed is that a bird siezes a resting insect too rapidly to be detected without the aid of a carefully designed experiment. In another moth, the Mottled Beauty (*Cleora repandata*), the gene producing melanism in the imago also confers superior hardiness upon the larvae, allowing them the better to withstand starvation, though it does not affect their colouring. Here again, melanics occur almost exclusively in the Lancashire and Yorkshire 'black country', and have not extended over the rest of the insect's range which includes the whole of England and Scotland. The reason why these dark forms have not replaced the normal ones throughout the whole country is presumably because they are so obvious against a normal background and therefore liable to a high death-rate from birds.

GENETIC IMPLICATIONS OF EVOLUTIONARY CHANGE

Attempts are sometimes made to measure the rates of evolution in wild populations. These have seldom met with much success, which is not surprising when it is realized how slow the process normally is. For it is very seldom that a particular combination of genes gives such an advantage to its possessor as to enable it to sweep through a population in a few generations, as occurred in the melanic form of the Peppered Moth. It can be calculated that a gene conferring only a 1 per cent advantage on a particular organism might be expected to increase the frequency of its appearance in the population from 1 per cent to 5 per cent in the course of about 160 generations. This is a mere trifle in terms of evolutionary time, and normally advances will take place much more slowly in the wild state.[1] (For further references see the Bibliography.)

SPECIALIZATION AND DISTRIBUTION

When evolving, it is normally an advantage for an organism to remain as generalized as possible so that it may become adapted to a wide range of conditions. Once committed to some special sort of existence, a species is usually incapable of retracing its steps and, if conditions change beyond its limited powers of adjustment, extinction will result. This extreme kind of adaptation is known as *specialization*, and is characteristic of such forms as gut parasites. For instance, the tapeworm *Taenia solium* is beautifully adapted to inhabit the alimentary canal of man, but as an adult can exist nowhere else. Improved sanitation and the introduction of vermifuges have thus rapidly brought about its extinction in this country.

On the other hand, man with his highly complex structure has attained a remarkably wide tolerance of environmental conditions. To-day, there are few places on the earth's surface which he cannot inhabit.

[1] It is now known that selective advantages of 30 per cent or more are quite common among polymorphic species such as the Peppered Moth. For further treatment of this subject see, Dowdeswell, W. H. (1958, 2nd edn.), *The Mechanism of Evolution*; Heinemann.

INFLUENCE OF SEASONAL CHANGE ON DISTRIBUTION

The area occupied by an animal species is never constant but fluctuates continually. The extent of the changes occurring annually is often small and difficult to detect. But within a locality a good deal of movement by animals is continually in progress, and this becomes particularly obvious at the beginning and end of winter. With the onset of colder conditions many species make special preparations for over-wintering, the significance of which will be discussed later.

For instance, some land animals hibernate among the vegetation or in holes in the ground, while many of the small aquatic invertebrates move from the surface waters to the shelter of the mud below.

The important point to realize here is that nearly all these changes involve some kind of movement from summer to winter quarters and back again. This results in the *seasonal distribution* characteristic of so many species. Such movement may be carried to extremes giving rise to a yearly *migration*; a subject considered further in Chapter III.

SOME GENERAL FEATURES OF ANIMAL COMMUNITIES

ANIMALS must be well fitted for the lives they lead if they are to endure the rigours of Natural Selection as described in Chapter II. They must also be either sufficiently tolerant or plastic to withstand the continual changes taking place around them. Such adjustments are achieved by *evolution*, for the better adapted individuals contribute more to posterity than their less successful competitors. Moreover, the hereditary element in variation ensures that their superior qualities shall in some measure be transmitted to their descendants, and accordingly spread through the population, so improving it to meet the demands of its environment. The measure of success achieved may be gauged by the various adaptations in structure and behaviour found among animals which have colonized different types of habitat. Some of these will be considered briefly in so far as they apply to animals in general.

PERIODS OF ACTIVITY AND REST

In most animal colonies a fairly clear-cut distinction can be drawn between the periods of activity and inactivity of different species. Anyone who has collected night-flying moths at a light trap, for instance, will know how the various species tend to have their own characteristic times of flight. Such periodic changes in behaviour are most obvious in land forms, but also occur to the same extent in aquatic animals with results often of great economic importance to man.

One of the most powerful factors influencing animal activity is the alternation of night and day. This may bring about the division of a colony into two more or less distinct elements, the nocturnal and diurnal communities. In a small wood for instance, we should expect to find by day such animals as squirrels, the majority of the birds, and a large number of arthropods including butterflies and spiders. At night the mammals would be represented by badgers and bats, the birds by owls and nightjars, and the arthropods by moths and woodlice. In addition, many molluscs would make their appearance, notably slugs.

As pointed out by Elton, such day and night communities may be regarded as independent to a large extent, but there must always be a certain amount of overlap between them. Thus some animals are active at dusk such as the Great Bat (*Nyctalus noctula*); others come out both by day and night such as the Vole and Nightingale. Some, although diurnal themselves, prey upon nocturnal forms, a typical instance being that of the Blackbird feeding on worms. The reverse is also found as when the Barn Owl raids sparrow roosts at night.

In aquatic habitats, variations in light intensity frequently bring about marked changes in the distribution of the minute animals (plankton) such as the water-fleas, which endeavour to occupy a zone of optimum illumination. This in turn influences the larger species which prey upon them.

INFLUENCE OF FOOD

One of the chief reasons for animal activity is to feed, and the presence of the correct food in adequate quantities largely determines whether a species can colonize a particular locality or not.

The requirements of different animals will be considered in detail in those chapters dealing with particular habitats (V–VIII). It is only necessary to add here that animals can be roughly classified on the basis of their diet as follows:

(*a*) Carnivores—those which prey on other animals.
(*b*) Herbivores—animals feeding exclusively on plants.
(*c*) Scavengers and detritus feeders. This group comprises

a wide range of organisms living on the dead remains of plants or animals in various stages of decomposition.

These categories are by no means absolute. For instance, carnivores generally include a certain amount of plant material in their diet. Similarly among scavengers and detritus feeders, it is often impossible to make a clear distinction between food which is fresh and that which has started to decompose. Furthermore, the animals themselves are frequently incapable of discriminating between them. This is particularly true of detritus (minute particles of decomposing plant and animal matter which accumulate at the bottom of static waters), which almost invariably includes some small living organisms as well.

FOOD RELATIONSHIPS AND FOOD CHAINS

The diet of any one animal community covers an immense range of organisms. Close study will generally show that a most intricate relationship exists between the different species and their foods. If we try to disentangle this web of relations we find that the different animals form, as it were, links in a chain of food. An example will make this clear. In any open woodland, aphids feed on the leaves of plants, ladybird beetles eat aphids, chaffinches eat ladybird beetles, and sparrow-hawks prey upon chaffinches. Here then is the food sequence: sparrow-hawks—chaffinches—ladybird beetles—aphids—plants. This is known as a *food chain*. Biotic relationships of this kind occur in all animal communities and form the basis of their food economy.

The study of food chains is a laborious but fascinating procedure. When a number of these are compared, they are found to have certain fundamental features in common.

(i) *Plants form the foundation of all food chains and are thus the basis of animal life.* This is due to the fact that plants are the only living organisms capable of building up their own food by the process of photosynthesis (autotrophic feeding).

(ii) *Food chains are much more complicated than they appear at first sight.* Nearly all animals utilize a variety of foods which are themselves often interdependent to a considerable extent. Thus each chain has many side branches which themselves link and subdivide to form a complicated network. The life-cycle of the herring, worked out in detail by Hardy (see Fig. 4), is a typical instance. When $\frac{1}{4}$ to $\frac{1}{2}$ inch long the young fish feeds largely on minute plants (diatoms), the larvae of molluscs, and various small crustaceans such as copepods. At the same time it is preyed upon by jelly-fish (Coelenterata), comb-jellies (Ctenophora), arrow worms (*Sagitta*) and the polychaete worm (*Tomopteris*). During the next stage of its life ($\frac{1}{2}$ to $1\frac{3}{4}$ inches) its food changes, being now confined entirely to copepods. Furthermore, it no longer constitutes the prey of worms. An increase in size from $1\frac{3}{4}$ to 5 inches results in little difference in diet except that this becomes more varied. At this stage the herring is free from invertebrate predators. From 5 inches in length until it attains full size, its food is not confined to copepods, but includes a vertebrate (young sand-eels), some of the larger crustaceans such as *Nyctiphanes* (Euphausiacea) and the tunicate *Oikopleura*. At each stage in the life-history there is a complex relationship of predator with predator and prey with prey, the bottom link in every instance being a primitive plant.

(iii) *In any one chain there are seldom more than five links, and generally only three.* This generalization holds good for the herring (see Fig. 4). As we ascend a food chain the size of each successive predator increases, until a final limit is reached when the animal is so large that it is not preyed upon at all. The magnitude of each step by which this increase in size occurs determines the number of possible links.

(iv) *Food chains involve a progressive increase in numbers and decrease in the size of animals.* At each stage in a food chain the number of predators becomes smaller as the animals get larger. This is due to their different rates of reproduction and the variable effects of Natural Selection. The mortality among small animals is always greater than that of large ones, hence their rate of reproduction must be correspondingly higher if they are to survive. Such a progression, or *pyramid of numbers* as

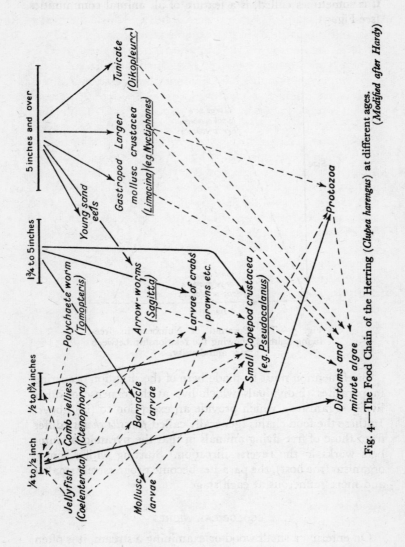

Fig. 4.—The Food Chain of the Herring (*Clupea harengus*) at different ages.
(*Modified after Hardy*)

it is sometimes called, is a feature of all animal communities (see Fig. 5).

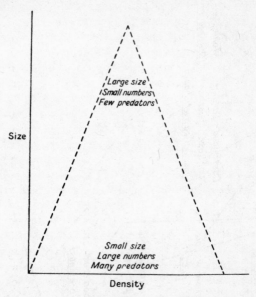

Fig. 5.—The Pyramid of Numbers in free-living animals, showing the relationship between size and density.

Brief mention must be made here of the situation occurring in parasites (individuals which live at the expense of other living organisms), which provide an exception to (iv) above. In these the food chains (generally called *parasite chains*) differ from those of free-living animals in that the pyramid of numbers works in the reverse direction. Starting with a single organism (the host), the parasites become progressively smaller and more numerous at each stage.

ECOLOGICAL NICHES

On entering a small wood or examining a stream, it is often possible to predict with some accuracy the species of animals likely to be found there. We do this instinctively by fitting the animals into their ecological picture largely on the basis of their feeding habits. The economy of any animal habitat is such that only a limited quantity of the various kinds of food is available; hence competition of varying intensity must develop between the different species. For instance, the birds of a certain locality might be divided roughly into carnivores and herbivores. The carnivore group might be further subdivisible into predators on other birds and small mammals (e.g. Sparrow-hawk and Buzzard) and fish-eaters such as the Kingfisher. The amount of competition among the insectivores might perhaps be greater than among the fish-eaters because of their higher density and a relatively less abundant supply of food. Limitation in the number of insectivores would also affect the number of other carnivores which could prey upon them.

Thus each individual or colony within a community eventually strikes a kind of equilibrium with its neighbours and settles down to occupy a definite economic position or *ecological niche*. Information of this kind is essential for the study of animal distribution and problems of population density.

OVERCROWDING AND UNDERCROWDING

The size of an animal population is governed by two opposing sets of factors. On the one hand there is reproduction and immigration tending to increase it, and on the other deaths and emigration having the reverse effect. The seasons of reproduction in all animals are influenced to a large extent by the climate. But when breeding, warm-blooded animals are generally better able to adapt themselves to varying climatic conditions than cold-blooded species. They may also be influenced indirectly, as, for instance, when adverse conditions restrict food supply and feeding activity. Thus some non-migratory arctic birds such as the Snowy Owl and Ptarmigan breed only once in two years, the intervening time being used to accumulate a sufficient reserve of energy.

The death-rate in animals is also governed by a variety of factors, the principal being predators, climatic change, and food supply. Here again, warm-blooded animals are at an advantage in being able to withstand a greater diversity of conditions.

Such continual changes in the environment are sometimes beneficial to the animals and sometimes not. One of their most obvious effects is on population density which tends to fluctuate in all species according to the prevailing climatic and biotic conditions.

THE SIZE OF ANIMAL POPULATIONS

In ecology, the size of a population can be expressed in several different ways. One method is to state its *density*. This is the number of individuals per unit area of habitat, and can be determined either from a number of subjective estimates by trained observers or by some method of random sampling. If such observations are continued over a period of time, it is possible to form some idea of the extent to which numbers are fluctuating. This method has obvious limitations. It provides no more than a series of rough averages, and tells us little about the distribution of the animals within the area as a whole. For populations are never uniformly distributed, and few habitats are equally suitable for colonization throughout their range.

Another way of measuring populations is by means of an average figure covering a comparatively wide area, say several square miles. This may include localities where a species reaches both its maximum and minimum numbers, and is known as the *average density*. For instance, the statement that there are 1,000 rabbits per square mile of country provides the ecologist with a useful guide in assessing the amount of colonization achieved by the species under varying conditions, i.e. its ability to adapt itself to those particular circumstances. If such counts are continued for some time they may provide useful information on fluctuations in numbers within the area. The economic importance of such estimates is sometimes great, say in enabling a farmer to decide on the measures necessary to control the rabbit as a pest.

In ecology, average densities have one serious drawback as a means of expressing numbers, namely that they can only be applied to specific areas and are of little value for comparing different communities. No two localities are exactly similar,

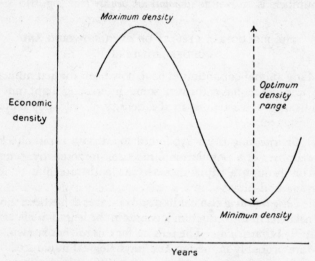

Fig. 6.—Diagram to illustrate cyclical fluctuation in the Economic Density of a typical animal population.

and hence the proportions of colonized and uncolonized land will invariably differ.

A more precise method is to calculate the *economic density*, that is to say the numbers per unit of *inhabited area*. An estimate of 1,000 rabbits per square mile of the country colonized is of value not only in studying fluctuations in the population, but also because it enables a valid comparison to be made between two totally different kinds of inhabited locality.

Sometimes the numbers of a population increase greatly, either for economic reasons or as a result of gregarious behaviour, as is found in some animals such as insects. Soon a point is reached at which overcrowding begins, when mass movement or a high mortality act as a kind of biological safety valve. This figure is known as the *maximum density*, and is important in the study of erratic movements and the spread of disease in animal communities. Conversely, the lowest density to which a population sinks at a particular reduction in numbers is known as its *minimum density* (see Fig. 6).

THE BIOLOGICAL RESULTS OF OVERCROWDING AND UNDERCROWDING

Many animal communities have now been studied numerically and these have thrown some interesting light on the significance of variations in the density of wild populations. For instance:

(i) *Overcrowding* is always found to cause a rapid check in the numbers of a population, either self-imposed by emigration or through a rapid increase in death-rate due to food shortage and disease.

(ii) *Undercrowding* also has its disadvantages as has been shown for instance, in the reduction it causes in the length of life of the Fruit Fly (*Drosophila*). The reasons for this are not known, but they are probably numerous and physiological in nature.

Small numbers inevitably cause difficulties in sexually reproducing organisms, since the two sexes are less likely to find one another when dispersed over a wide area. Psychology may also play a part in such circumstances as is shown by the behaviour of certain sea birds. In these the stimulus to pair is induced not only by the single male or female, but by the cumulative effect of the other individuals in the vicinity. Severe fluctuations in numbers may thus be a great danger to the population as a whole, for when the density falls below a critical level, the remaining birds cease to pair and a sudden collapse results. Circumstances such as these may account for the extraordinary variation in colour and marking of the male Ruff (*Philomachus pugnax*), in which the females are stimulated by the variety of colour and diversity of display going on around them on the common courting ground. If this is so, selection would tend to favour any hereditary constitution providing the greatest variability, and hence the biggest psychological effect.

The extent of a habitat may also play a part in determining the length of life of its occupants. Thus animals inhabiting a small area are liable to a higher death-rate in nature than those occupying a larger one. This is partly due to inbreeding, but also because a higher proportion of the individuals must approach the perimeter and be exposed to the less favourable conditions occurring there, and the possibility of loss from the colony. A small piece of ground will also tend to be of a more uniform nature than a large one, and hence provide poorer facilities for colonization and survival. Furthermore, small populations are exposed to much greater danger than large ones when their numbers reach their lowest level in a fluctuation.

(iii) *Slight crowding* acts as a stimulus to further increase in numbers. This is probably due to the increased activity which must result from greater competition for a limited food supply; an effect which may in its turn influence the rate of breeding.

Most animal colonies have an *optimum density range* (see Fig. 6). Below this they become subject to the disadvantages of undercrowding, and above it overcrowding begins. Within these limits the numbers fluctuate continually. The term *optimum density* is also sometimes applied to populations, and is the figure beyond which biological checks such as food shortage and disease begin to exert their effects (synonymous with *maximum density*). A species seldom remains at its optimum density for any length of time.

WEIGHT OF POPULATIONS AND THEIR FOOD

Another method of expressing animal density is in terms of weight, to which so far only scant attention has been paid. If the average weight of a species and its density are known, the latter may be expressed in terms of bulk (either living or dry) per unit area. Thus Alexander found that on certain farmland over a period of three months, the bird population per acre (living weight) averaged 57 kilogrammes in October, 47 kilogrammes in November, and 32 kilogrammes in February. This method could be extended to cover a whole community including many different species, and although of limited value it has certain advantages. In particular, it enables a more direct comparison to be made of the bulk of food consumed in different localities. It also provides a rough means of determining the ability of a habitat to support an animal colony at different times of the year.[1] This applies particularly to the study of seasonal fluctuations in the minute organisms (plankton) occurring in static waters.

FLUCTUATION IN NUMBERS

Animal communities fluctuate continually within their optimum density range, and their numbers are held in check by the various biological factors already discussed. Sometimes, for reasons to be considered shortly, the numbers get out of control and increase at a great rate. This occurs in the Gipsy Moth (*Lymantria dispar*) which, although of little economic importance in southern Europe, is a pest in Canada. The activities of its larvae cause much damage to the leaves of trees and consequent loss of valuable timber. When local food supplies are exhausted the larvae, if not fully grown, frequently indulge in mass movement to new feeding grounds. Some idea of the size of their swarms can be gained from the fact that trains on the Canadian Pacific Railway have been halted on occasions when travelling uphill, the wheels of the engine skidding on the squashed bodies of millions of caterpillars. In this country, many animals ranging from field mice to echinoderms (e.g. *Psammechinus miliaris*) are liable to similar outbreaks.

Study of these violent fluctuations reveals two important facts about them:

[1] This is sometimes referred to as its *productivity*.

(i) Periods of superabundance are always followed by intervals of rarity. This might be expected when food is short, disease probably widespread, and the numbers of parasites and predators are on the increase.

(ii) Fluctuations are often regular in their occurrence. For instance, in Great Britain the Short-Tailed Field Mouse (*Microtus*) exhibits a four-yearly cycle. In Canada the Snow-shoe Rabbit, Lynx, and Red Fox all fluctuate over approximately eleven-yearly periods, as is shown by the records of the Hudson Bay Company (see Fig. 7).

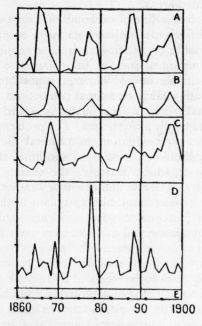

Fig. 7.—Fluctuation in the numbers of northern mammals. The diagrams show the number of skins brought into the Hudson Bay Company from 1860 to 1900. Note the striking eleven-yearly peaks in the Snow-Shoe Rabbit (*a*), the Lynx (*b*), and the Red Fox (*c*). Oscillations in the Arctic Fox (*d*) are three-yearly.

(*After Hewitt and Elton*)

The causes of fluctuations in population density, whether regular or not, are still largely unknown. Their effect is often widespread as is shown by the eleven-yearly maxima in the numbers of the Snow-Shoe Rabbit, Lynx, and Red Fox which correspond in a striking way (see Fig. 7). Their smaller three-year oscillations are also concurrent with those of the Arctic Fox. Among butterflies, too, the Camberwell Beauty (*Nymphalis antiopa*) in Scandinavia, the Bath White (*Pontia daplidice*) and Queen of Spain Fritillary (*Argynnis lathonia*) in Mediterranean regions are all subject to coincident migration, indicating a common agency at work in the two widely separated areas.

The most obvious line of explanation is on a climatic basis. In fact it is difficult to see what other factor or set of conditions could be capable of exerting such far-reaching effects. In certain circumstances, such as the occurrence of an exceptionally dry summer or cold winter, it is possible to detect the effect of climatic change on animal populations. But attempts during normal years to link fluctuations with the weather have so far met with little success. The problem is a complex one involving a combination of physical factors, such as temperature, humidity, wind, and sunshine, also current in aquatic habitats, which constitute the climatic environment of a community. The rate and extent of weather changes must also be taken into account, also variations in the sequence of these changes from year to year. Evidence suggests that such effects are cumulative and may therefore exert their influence over a period of several years. There is also reason to believe that some organisms are sensitive to environmental changes which are too small to be recorded by normal meteorological methods. Their effect is also probably cumulative. For instance, recent studies suggest that the retraction and expansion of glaciers may provide a sensitive means of detecting minute long-term climatic changes. Such data have yet to be applied on a wide scale, but we know that they can already be correlated with the fluctuations in several species of British butterflies which appear to be influenced by the varying conditions.

Some mathematical evidence suggests that fluctuations, at any rate within the optimum density range, may be the natural outcome of the structure of animal communities themselves. In other words such cycles may be self-induced. But it is difficult to see how such an explanation could hold good except within certain narrow limits, and then only in conjunction with the other ecological factors already discussed.

The solution of the problem of animal fluctuations is of the greatest economic importance to man. This would enable him to predict periods of abundance and scarcity in vital industries such as fisheries and plan accordingly. Where populations fluctuate regularly, as in some of the fur-bearing mammals of Canada, a measure of prediction is already possible. Such circumstances are, however, exceptional, and our knowledge of them has been acquired only after many years of extensive records by the Hudson Bay and other companies.

EVOLUTIONARY SIGNIFICANCE OF FLUCTUATION IN NUMBERS

Numerical fluctuations in wild organisms provide exceptional opportunities for evolution. The greater the increase in numbers, so the better will be the chance of the different genetic factors being tried out in a wide variety of gene complexes. Beneficial variations may thus result. Some of the genes involved will be rare and exert only a small effect. These may, however, prove of considerable evolutionary value once they are given the opportunity of spreading within the population.

The advantages gained in this way will not only be visible ones (phenotypic) such as colour, size, and shape, but also constitutional (physiological) such as the hardier melanic form of the Large Mottled Beauty Moth (*Cleora repandata*). It has been pointed out that a gene causing a physiological advantage of this kind may easily spread through a population, even though any external characteristics which it may control as well are ecologically useless to the animal concerned. In large populations, a greater amount of variability among the organisms is possible than in small ones because:

(i) They afford better opportunities for the spread and establishment of genes having small but beneficial effects.

(ii) They can hold more 'neutral' genes in reserve, whose influence in existing circumstances is neither beneficial nor disadvantageous, for adaptation to changing environmental conditions.

The testing of such hypotheses experimentally in wild populations is a difficult matter. For it is seldom possible to find a species where the population fluctuates in numbers and at the same time exhibits sufficient variability for small evolutionary changes to be detected. It has been done by H. D. Ford and E. B. Ford in a colony of the Marsh Fritillary Butterfly (*Euphydryas aurinia*) which breeds once a year. They found that numbers increased from rarity to great abundance over a period of some four years, remaining thereafter at much the same level during the observations, which were continued for a further eleven years. Before this fluctuation a constant form of the butterfly existed, even slight divergences from it being rare. But the four years of rapid increase were accompanied by a remarkable outburst of variability, hardly any two specimens being alike. Many of these showed great differences from the normal type. Many deformities were found, the degree of malformation being closely correlated with the amount of variation. During subsequent years the species settled down once more to a comparatively uniform appearance; this, however, was markedly different from the original.

The observed facts fit in closely with genetic theory. The sudden outburst of variability associated with deformities is exactly what might have been expected, for ideal conditions existed here for a variety of genes to be tried out in new and unaccustomed genetic combinations as a result of the rapid multiplication in numbers.

Subdivision of a population into a number of isolated or semi-isolated communities also favours evolutionary progress not, as Sewall Wright thought, because these become more variable, but because of the diverse habitats to which each group can be adapted.

Processes such as these are constantly bringing about evolution in wild populations, but the changes are generally so slow and their magnitude so small that they are not easily detected experimentally.

MOVEMENT

The ability to move is a feature of all animals. The significance of movement in colonization has already been considered (see p. 17). But in all animals increase in range is generally an incidental outcome of moves initiated for other reasons, namely:

   (i) As a result of the action of wind and water currents.
   (ii) To obtain food or avoid predators.
   (iii) To prevent overcrowding.
   (iv) To breed.

DISPERSAL BY WIND AND WATER CURRENTS

In entomological literature, there are many accounts from Britain and elsewhere of remarkable invasions by huge numbers of small insects which have been blown along by the wind. Passive dispersal of this kind is often described as 'drift'. In this country, it has long been known that aphids ('green-fly' and 'black-fly') are subject to mass transportation by air currents, and these outbursts of activity have been shown to occur with a regular periodicity during the summer and autumn months. One of the most striking instances of aphid drift is that recorded by Elton from Spitsbergen in 1924 when he found large numbers of these insects on the snow. From the direction of the wind, it was clear that they must have originated from the mainland 800 miles away.

More lately, detailed studies have been made of insect

swarms occurring at various altitudes. With the aid of nets towed by aircraft, or attached to balloons and tall masts, it has been shown that many small species are habitually dispersed by the wind. Some of these are pests of great economic importance. For instance, the young larvae of the Gipsy Moth (*Lymantria dispar*) (see p. 42) possess long hairs which greatly increase their resistance to the air; these have been captured at a height of 2,000 feet. Recent estimates of this 'aerial plankton' suggest that its numbers are immense. Thus Hardy and Milne found at Hull, between May and October, that a column of air one mile square from a height between 1,000 and 2,000 feet, contained an average population of a quarter of a million insects.

Similarly, the density of aquatic plankton may reach huge proportions and its dispersal by currents is a characteristic feature of rivers and the sea. We have already seen how these minute organisms play a vital part in the food chains of the larger animals, many of which, such as fishes, are of great importance to man. The various ecological factors influencing the density and distribution of plankton are considered in detail in Chapters VI and VIII.

MOVEMENT AND FEEDING

Movement by animals in search of food is generally of an erratic kind. Some species such as gannets cover great distances (up to 100 miles), others tend to base themselves on a small locality and seldom move far from it. This is frequently true of small passerine birds such as tits. Many marine animals such as the herring lead a permanently nomadic existence, their distribution depending on that of the plankton which forms a vital link in their food chain. This fact is of great economic importance, for by means of plankton recorders it can be ascertained whether a certain area is worth fishing or not.

The principal factors influencing this kind of movement are the availability of food, the existence of predators, and the amount of competition by other animals occupying the same or closely related ecological niches.

In some species the climate plays a large part in determining the distribution of food, and hence the distances over which animals must move to obtain it. The Caribou in North America provides a typical example where seasonal changes result in a move northwards in spring and south again in the autumn, a heavy extermination of stragglers by wolves taking place on each journey.

MOVEMENT DUE TO OVERCROWDING

An excessive increase in the numbers of an animal colony results in food shortage which is frequently accompanied by a high incidence of disease. In higher animals such as birds and mammals, such conditions often exert a psychological as well as a physiological effect. This causes a general restlessness sometimes amounting to hysteria, and an overwhelming urge to leave the community.

Among mammals, a well-known instance is the Lemming (*Myodes lemmus*), a small rodent inhabiting the barren arctic country of eastern Scandinavia, whose numbers fluctuate at approximately four-yearly intervals. When these reach a critical high level the greater part of the population becomes possessed with a desire to move, as Elton has put it, like 'a rather tragic procession of refugees, with all the obsessed behaviour of an unwanted stranger in a populous land, going blindly on to various deaths'. The reasons for this behaviour are not known for certain, but lack of food does not seem to be a primary cause. No doubt disease plays some part. Perhaps this is an example of the kind of mob psychology already mentioned, which results in an hysterical urge obsessing almost the whole population. Once on the move, the animals proceed rapidly down the western valleys endeavouring to cross any obstacles in their path, including large rivers. Vast numbers perish on the way and the survivors reach the sea where they eventually drown. These emigrations seem to have no effect on the range eventually occupied by the species, and repopulation takes place from the few individuals which remain behind in their old home. An interesting feature of the Lemming's unusual behaviour is the psychological change which accompanies it; for a normally shy and timid creature changes into a bold and at times almost pugnacious animal. The causes underlying this change are as yet unknown.

Some species of birds such as Pallas's Sandgrouse (*Syrrhaptes paradoxus*), a resident of eastern Europe and Central Asia, behave in a somewhat similar way. Stragglers from its periodic irruptions in numbers sometimes reach our coasts, but never succeed in establishing themselves here.

Similar outbreaks occur among invertebrates. For instance, the African Migratory Locust (*Locusta migratoria*) swarms periodically as a result of environmental changes, the nature of which are not known for certain. Physiological and structural changes in the animal are so extensive that the migratory and non-migratory forms were at one time thought to be different species. Many other insects such as butterflies are subject to the same kind of outbursts in numbers, but these are rarely accompanied by any apparent alterations in the structure of the animals.

MOVEMENT FOR BREEDING

The term migration is interpreted in a variety of different ways. Here it will be used to denote an outward and return journey associated with breeding. Such movements always occur with a regular frequency and generally correspond to seasonal changes.

Migratory behaviour by animals is remarkable in many ways and raises numerous biological problems. The movements involved are exceptional and generally unrelated to those taking place at any phase of the animal's life other than at breeding time. An immense amount has been written about migration, far more than on all other aspects of animal movement put together. Many examples could be quoted, but they will be restricted to four typical instances occurring respectively in a mammal, a bird, a fish, and an invertebrate (crab).

MIGRATION IN A MAMMAL (FUR SEAL)

Among land mammals migration is generally unspectacular and no examples of any note occur in Britain. Some marine species, however, such as the Fur Seal (*Callorhinus alascanus*) perform remarkable journeys. The females and immature males of this species winter in southern California, while the mature males are to be found in the Gulf of Alaska (see Fig. 8). At the beginning of the breeding season the mature males move northwards to a group of small islands (Pribilof Islands) north of the Aleutians. The females also migrate there from southern California, a journey of some 3,000 miles. Pairing has already occurred before the previous journey south, and by the time the females reach their northern limit again they are pregnant and give birth to their young a few days after arrival. After weaning, impregnation occurs once more, and the females set off southwards accompanied by their young, the mature males remaining to migrate later towards the Gulf of Alaska. How the seals find their way over such immense distances and to such a remote breeding ground remains a mystery, as do many feats of navigation among migratory animals.

MIGRATION IN A BIRD (SWALLOW)

Movement among birds provides some of the classic examples of migration (see Bibliography for further references).

Nearly all birds indulge in some seasonal movement ranging from journeys of a few hundred feet up and down a mountain side, to flights of several thousand miles across vast tracts of featureless ocean. Even among flightless species such as penguins, movement to the breeding grounds may require a

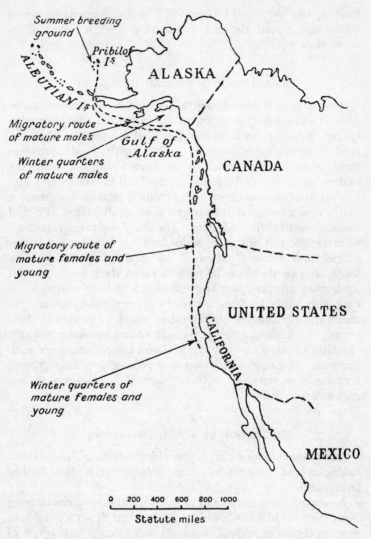

Fig. 8.—Migration routes of the Fur Seal (*Callorhinus alascanus*).

journey of several hundred miles accomplished by swimming
or on foot.

Birds usually breed in the coldest part of their range; thus in
the northern hemisphere there is a general movement north in

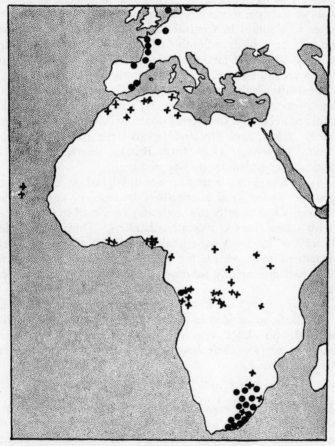

Fig. 9.—Migration of the Swallow (*Hirundo rustica*) as shown by the recovery
of ringed birds. Black dots indicate nestlings ringed in Great Britain; crosses
refer to those marked on the continent of Europe.

(*After Witherby, Leach, and Schüz*)

spring and south in autumn. In this way the rigours of a
northern winter are avoided while full benefit is derived from
the longer summer hours. One of our best-known migrants,
described at length by Aristotle, is the Swallow (*Hirundo
rustica*). During our summer its range extends across almost the
whole of Europe, western Asia, and north-west Africa; in the
winter it is found in Central and South Africa, also India.
The capture of birds in South Africa marked with British rings
has established the fact that some of our summer residents
enjoy a second summer after leaving our shores (see Fig. 9).

The swallow's time-table of migration is on the whole remarkably constant from year to year. It reaches Gibraltar by the
middle of February, southern France by mid-March, England
in early April, and Scotland towards the end of the same
month. Movement south from Britain, started in July, is
practically complete by mid-September.

The journeys are normally accomplished at altitudes of
3,000 feet or less, and at speeds of between 20 and 50 miles
per hour. Occasionally the birds may be forced to fly at great
heights when crossing mountain barriers. Thus 'Le Col des
Hirondelles' in the Alps, a peak 11,370 feet above sea-level,
is so named on account of the dead swallows once found there
which had presumably become casualties on their migratory
journey.

The sense or instinct which enables an adult swallow to find
its way back to its former nesting site year after year is still
unknown. So also is the way in which some young birds
manage to perform their first migratory flight unaccompanied
by their parents.[1]

PHYSIOLOGY AND THE IMPULSE TO MIGRATE

Physiological processes undoubtedly play an important part
in bird migration just as they do in the erratic movements of
the lemming (see p. 49). Rowan's work on the Canadian
Junco (*Junco hyemalis*) has thrown considerable light on the
situation. He showed that birds which had been subjected

[1] For an excellent summary of recent work on this subject see, Matthews,
G. V. T. (1955), *Bird Navigation*; Cambridge.

during the winter to an artificially increased amount of illumination (thus simulating spring and early summer conditions) could be induced to migrate prematurely. Artificial
exercise imposed on the birds by keeping them in a cage with a
moving perch which prevented them from sleeping was found
to have the same effect. In both instances, dissection showed
the gonads to have developed to the condition characteristic
of the breeding season.

Such explanations of the impulse to migrate are only of
limited application, for they could not account for the northward
movement of birds wintering in the tropics or for the behaviour
of such species as the gannet which migrates before it is
sexually mature. The problem of migration in animals is
exceedingly complex and, as yet, we have barely reached the
fringe of its solution.

MIGRATION IN A FISH (EEL)

Many fish perform long migratory journeys, a well-known
example being the Eel (*Anguilla vulgaris*). This moves from the
fresh waters of rivers to the sea in order to breed.

Migration is accompanied by both structural and physiological changes. The colour alters from a yellowish to a silvery
appearance, the eyes enlarge and the snout becomes more
pointed. At the same time the reproductive organs develop
and feeding ceases. By some unknown means the Eels of the
British and Scandinavian rivers find their way to areas of the
Caribbean Sea where they spawn at great depths. Afterwards
the adults die, the eggs giving rise to small, *leptocephalus*
larvae. These return slowly eastwards, the first part of their
journey being accomplished mainly by passive drifting. After
three years they undergo a rapid metamorphosis into elvers
about three inches long and once more repopulate the rivers.

Some fish such as the Pacific Salmon (*Onchorhynchus*) are
known to return frequently to the same rivers in which they
passed their early life. How this homing behaviour is achieved
still remains largely a mystery.

MIGRATION IN AN INVERTEBRATE (CRAB)

Among invertebrates migration is not uncommon, but the distances travelled are never as great as those of vertebrates. The Edible Crab (*Cancer pagurus*) is a typical instance (see Fig. 10). In September it moves from the tidal zone to water of 20 to 30 fathoms depth where spawning takes place. From February to March a return movement occurs, and by the beginning of May the crabs, bearing fertilized eggs, have reached the warm inshore waters once more. Here the larvae hatch and spend the early part of their lives. The following autumn the cycle is repeated.

Fig. 10.—Seasonal movement in the Edible Crab (*Cancer pagurus*).

Similar movements occur among many other invertebrates including molluscs, crustaceans, and insects[1] (see Bibliography for references).

[1] For an outstanding recent account of insect migration see, Williams, C. B. (1958), *Insect Migration*; Collins.

CHAPTER IV

SPECIAL ANIMAL RELATIONSHIPS

THE degree of intimacy in the relationships of the animals inhabiting a particular locality varies greatly. The majority can be regarded as free-living, that is to say, they are not dependent on the occurrence in the same area of any one particular animal species or group of species. Their range is determined mainly by climatic factors, living space, and the availability of an adequate food supply, which generally comprises a fair variety of other animals or plants or a combination of both. It is with such species that we are largely concerned when studying elementary ecology.

Some animals, however, are far more fastidious in their requirements, and have become dependent for their survival on varying degrees of co-operation with members of one or more other species. Such 'special relationships' often raise interesting ecological problems, some of which will be discussed in this chapter; furthermore, they may be of considerable economic importance.

Since the majority of these partnerships must have evolved independently of each other, it is not surprising to find that the extent to which their members rely on one another varies considerably. Thus on the one hand we find one organism serving merely as a kind of anchorage for another (epizoic condition), while on the other it may harbour its partner permanently inside it (parasitic and symbiotic conditions). Between these extremes a great many intermediate phases may be found, so that the following classification must be regarded as a somewhat arbitrary one.

EPIZOITES

An animal associated with another (the host) for the purpose of anchorage or protection only is known as an *epizoite*. Such

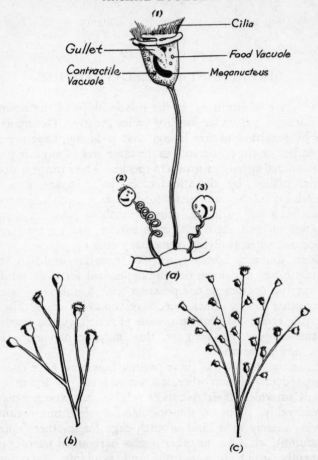

Fig. 11.—(a) Typical Vorticellid protozoan: (1) much enlarged; (2) contracted (×100); (3) undergoing binary fission (×100). (b) Epistylis (×50). (c). Carchesium (×50).

an association is never very intimate and involves no physiological partnership of any kind. Furthermore, epizoites are generally facultative, that is to say, they are also able to lead a free-living existence if conditions demand it. There are many instances of this kind of association among both terrestrial and aquatic animals, the essential features in all of them being:

(a) The epizoite may have numerous different hosts (i.e. it is not *specific* in its requirements).

(b) The host is inevitably larger than the epizoite.

(c) The benefits, as far as can be ascertained, are frequently one-sided and in favour of the epizoite, although the host does not appear to lose by the partnership.

Some good examples of epizoites readily obtainable for study, can be found on the Freshwater Shrimp (*Gammarus pulex*), also on many aquatic insect nymphs such as those of the Mayfly *Ecdyonurus*. These support various epizoic ciliate protozoans notably the vorticellids *Carchesium* and *Epistylis* (see Fig. 11). They are generally to be found in small colonies attached to the legs of the host by their slender stalks, and can easily be distinguished from one another, for the stalks of *Carchesium* constantly elongate and contract while those of *Epistylis* do not. As far as is known the epizoites confer no particular advantage or disadvantage on their host, while they themselves presumably benefit from the protection and anchorage provided, also no doubt from any stray food-particles escaping from the larger animal's mouth.

PARASITES

An animal may be regarded as a parasite if it exists partially or entirely at the expense of another living organism. This kind of association is naturally a very variable one. Sometimes the parasite resides only on the exterior of its host such as a flea on a dog (*ectoparasite*). On the other hand, it may find its way by devious means into the host's internal tissues and live there, such as the Liver Fluke in sheep (*endoparasite*). Between these two extremes all grades of parasitism occur. Some animals are ectoparasitic at one stage in their life-history and endoparasitic at another, others are parasitic at one time and free-living at another and so on. The

[1] For a detailed study of parasites see, Cameron, T. W. M. (1956), *Parasites and Parasitism*; Methuen.

subdivision into ectoparasites and endoparasites is therefore by no means absolute, but none the less serves as a useful rough classification for descriptive purposes.

ECTOPARASITES

Parasitism sometimes occurs in the young stage only, a notorious example being the Cuckoo in which a deceptive resemblance sometimes occurs between the egg of the parasite

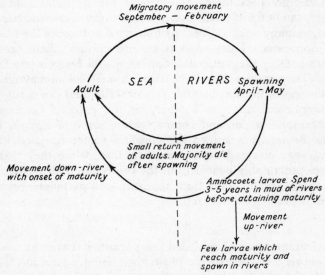

Fig. 12.—The life-cycle of the Lampern (*Lampetra fluviatilis*), a typical ectoparasite deriving both nourishment and transport from its host.

and those of the intended foster parent. Here the association consists merely in the host supplying the young cuckoo with the food destined for its own offspring which are usually ejected from the nest by the parasite at an early stage.

Often the association between ectoparasite and host is of a more intimate kind and may involve actual physiological union, such as occurs in the adult Lampern or River

Lamprey (*Lampetra fluviatilis*). The name Lampern is perhaps preferable as there is now no doubt that a considerable part of its life is spent in the sea (see Fig. 12). The larval stage (*ammocoete*) is worm-like, toothless, and lives a burrowing existence in the mud of rivers feeding on various organic matter. In the adult, the feeding mechanism is highly specialized, consisting of a circular mouth which can act as a sucker, through which protrudes a rasping tongue covered with horny teeth. It attacks various species of teleost fish, boring its way into the body-wall by means of its tongue and adhering with its circular mouth. In this way it obtains food and also a ready means of transport. Neither of these is indispensable to the Lampern for it is a good swimmer and also capable of feeding on various small animals living on the bottom of rivers and in the shallow sea, also on fish spawn. An animal of this kind capable of two alternative types of existence is known as a *facultative parasite*.

Ectoparasites are generally invertebrates, particularly insects, a typical example, where incidentally both young and adult are parasites, being the Biting Lice (Mallophaga). These are small flat-bodied insects which infest various species of birds and mammals. They do not suck blood but live on feathers, hair, and other epidermal products. The harm they cause to the host results not so much from denudation in infested areas of the body, as from the extreme skin irritation which they set up. The dust-baths taken by many birds are chiefly for the purpose of removing Mallophaga. It has been shown that the parasites are incapable of surviving for long after the death of the host, a period of about three days being the maximum. The whole of their life history takes place among the feathers and transmission is presumably achieved by direct contact between one bird and another. It is interesting to note that the various species of Mallophaga are invariably associated each with a few, or even a single species of bird.

ENDOPARASITES

The association between endoparasites and their hosts is invariably much more intimate than that found in ectoparasites. Again, parasitism by no means always occurs in the adult phase. A typical instance where the young stage (larva) only is a parasite is provided by the warble flies of the genus *Hypoderma* (see Plate 3, at p. 64). The adult flies are active during the summer months, and lay their eggs on the hair of cattle to which they adhere with remarkable firmness making them resistant to the most violent scratching. After hatching, the young larvae burrow their way through the skin of the host and eventually arrive in the muscles of the back near the vertebral column. Here they form swellings or 'warbles' and remain until the following May or even later. By this time the larvae are fully grown and they now burrow their way outwards, passing through the skin and falling to the ground where they pupate in the earth. After a period of 5–6 weeks, the adult flies emerge and the life-cycle is completed. The economic importance of warble flies is very great, for if infection is severe they may cause immense harm in perforating the hide, retarding bodily development of the host, and reducing milk production. It is estimated that our annual losses in leather alone amount to the equivalent of 10,000,000 shoe soles. Furthermore, unless attacked at an early stage, the larva is very difficult to kill. Occasionally larvae find their way into the central nervous system and cause the death of the animal concerned. In general, however, although endoparasites inflict varying degrees of harm on their hosts they seldom kill them, or if they do, this does not occur until after they themselves have successfully reproduced.

The majority of endoparasites are parasitic as adults. In many forms such as most of the roundworms (Nematoda), their young stages are free-living; in others they are themselves parasites in other animals which may act as temporary quarters during part of the life-cycle (*secondary hosts*), or merely as a means of dispersal (*vectors*). A typical endoparasite employing a secondary host is the trematode worm *Distomum macrostomum*, a fluke found in the gut of thrushes (see Fig. 13). The eggs of the parasite are dispersed with the faeces of the bird, and if eaten by a snail such as *Helix aspersa* they develop into a larva, the sporocyst, which finds its way to the tentacles where it develops pigment as brightly coloured bands of red and green. The

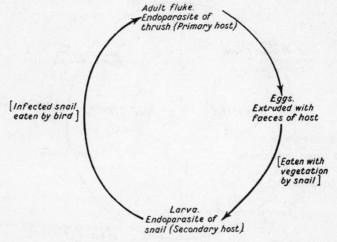

Fig. 13.—Life-cycle of the fluke *Distomum macrostomum*, an endoparasite of thrushes.

presence of the sporocyst prevents the snail from withdrawing its tentacles which then serve as an admirable advertisement of its presence to other birds. If the snail is then eaten, the larvae, which by now have developed within the sporocyst, are liberated giving rise to young flukes.

Sometimes parasites may exhibit both ecto- and endoparasitic phases and, furthermore, may undergo remarkable alterations in structure when changing from one to the other. They may also cause correspondingly great modifications in their hosts. Some striking examples of this are to be found in the Crustacea (see Fig. 14). Among the parasitic barnacles (Rhizocephala) for instance, the genus *Sacculina* parasitizes the

Spider Crab (*Inachus*), on which it appears as a soft, oval, yellow body under the tail, bearing no structural resemblance whatever to an adult barnacle which its larval form shows it to be. The yellow mass is, in fact, nothing more than an hermaphroditic assemblage of genital organs with roots entering the host and spreading throughout its tissues. The

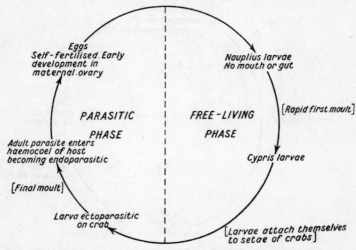

Fig. 14.—Life-cycle of the crustacean *Sacculina*, an endoparasite of certain crabs.

self-fertilized eggs give rise to *nauplius* larvae characteristic of normal barnacles except that they are devoid of mouth and gut. These soon moult forming *cypris* larvae, which, if they find a crab, attach themselves by means of their antennules to the setae of the body. At this stage the animal is an ecto-parasite. The larva soon penetrates the body-wall of the host at the base of the setae whereupon a rapid development takes place. The larval skin is thrown off and an undifferentiated mass of tissue develops which bores its way into the haemocoele of the crab, eventually being carried in the blood to the anterior regions of the gut. Here it puts out absorptive pro-cesses, growing backwards to the region between the thorax

(*a*)   The adult fly (*H. lineatum*). ×2½ approx.

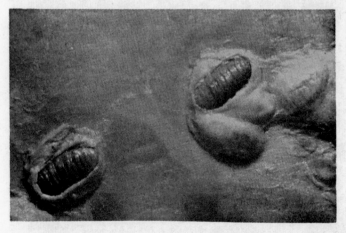

(*b*)   The underside of a hide with encysted larvae of *H. bovis*
forming warbles. Natural size. The larva is an endoparasite
of cattle

3.   THE WARBLE FLY (*Hypoderma*)

4. SPECIAL PROCRYPTIC COLORATION IN A BIRD. THE WOODCOCK (*Scolopax rusticola*) ON ITS NEST

and abdomen. It is now a true endoparasite and is sometimes known as a *Sacculina interna*. At the next moult of the crab, the parasite becomes loosened by ferments which it secretes and bulges on to the surface as the characteristic adult phase (see Fig. 15). As might be expected, the presence of *Sacculina* brings

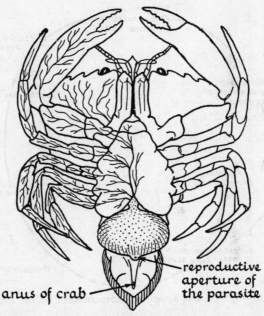

anus of crab ⎯ reproductive aperture of the parasite

Fig. 15.—A Shore Crab (*Carcinus*) bearing a *Sacculina*, seen from below with the abdomen extended. The root-like processes of the parasite rami-fying through the tissues of the host are shown on the right side only.

(*After Yonge*)

about remarkable changes in its host which may eventually cause its death, although it is not in the interest of the parasite that this should occur prematurely. The first effect is to inhibit further moulting. Subsequently, sterility results followed by a kind of parasitic castration in which various changes occur in the external features. In the female crab these are only slight and amount to little more than a minor reduction of the appendages concerned in egg laying. The male, however, undergoes marked sex reversal, assuming many female characteristics including a reduction of the large claws (chelae), broadening of the abdominal region, and the development of typical egg-laying appendages.

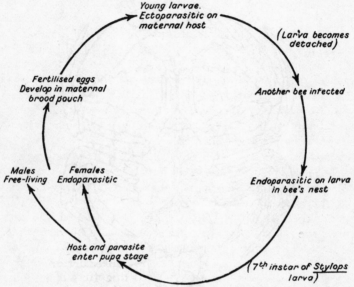

Fig. 16.—Life-cycle of *Stylops*, an endoparasite of the bee *Andrena*.

Even more striking effects of endoparasites upon their hosts are found among insects, particularly in the Order Strepsiptera[1] where various members of the genus *Stylops* parasitize numerous Hymenoptera such as the bee *Andrena* (see Fig. 16). During their early life the young larvae of the parasite exist on the same host as their mother, but are eventually dispersed, either by direct contact with another bee or by being brushed off on a flower, and thence infecting a new individual. The next step towards endoparasitism differs from that of *Sacculina* for, once

[1] A small group closely related to the beetles (Order Coleoptera).

arrived in the bee's nest, the young *Stylops* seeks out a larva and burrows through its body-wall. Soon afterwards, moulting occurs, and the parasite becomes a legless grub, maggot-like in appearance. Unlike *Sacculina* the larva does not penetrate the tissues of the host, but lives in the haemocoele absorbing blood through its thin cuticle. By the 7th instar of *Stylops* the host has entered on the pupal stage, and the parasitic larva now works its way outwards and protrudes between the 4th and 5th abdominal segments. At this stage pupation occurs. The males later emerge as free-living individuals, but only survive for a few hours after liberation from their hosts. The female remains permanently endoparasitic, only the cephalothorax being visible externally, which protrudes through the body-wall of the adult host. The latter may harbour a number of these parasites, as many as thirty-one larvae having been isolated from a single individual.

Stylops exerts a profound effect on the host in both sexes, unlike *Sacculina* whose influence is largely restricted to the male crab. In the male, the light yellow colour of the head is much reduced towards the darker female condition, also the sting and copulatory organs are poorly developed. In the female the pollen collecting apparatus is diminished, so that the hind legs resemble the male condition; also the colour of the head tends to become more yellow. In both sexes, therefore, a certain degree of sex-reversal results. Furthermore, as we have seen, the parasite itself also undergoes considerable modification in that only one sex (the male) is ever free-living.

CHARACTERISTICS OF PARASITES

In order to be a successful parasite, an animal must be able to co-ordinate closely its own life-cycle and structure with those of its host. This calls for certain special adaptations.

In the first place it may have to undergo certain structural modifications, particularly if it is an endoparasite, in order to enable it to feed, attach itself, or reproduce. Structures evolved for such purposes are said to be specialized, and most parasites exhibit *specialization* to some extent. The rasping mouth of the

Lampern is a typical example, also the head (scolex) of tapeworms equipped with hooks and suckers for attachment to the
host's gut-wall. Gut parasites in general are faced with the
peculiar problem of withstanding the action of the digestive
juices of the host. In a tapeworm, specialization also involves
the secretion of anti-ferments which neutralize the enzymes in
its immediate vicinity, and the production of a protective layer
of mucus. Evidence of this is provided by the fact that dead
tapeworms are readily digested.

The parasitic roundworms (Nematoda) are an interesting
group, for in spite of the fact that they have succeeded in
colonizing a great variety of hosts, their general structure has
remained remarkably uniform and lacking in extreme specialization. They appear to have evolved successfully a bodily
organization suitable both for a free-living and parasitic
existence, and able to adapt itself to greatly varying conditions.
They are without doubt one of the most successful and ubiquitous groups of animal parasites.

Another vital problem concerning endoparasites in particular
is that of reproduction; for once isolated inside the host,
difficulties in the liberation and dispersal of eggs must inevitably arise. Even when these have been overcome there is still
often only a remote possibility of the eggs or young ever reaching another suitable habitat. In fact, reproduction under
such conditions is an extremely hazardous and wasteful
process. To counteract this, all internal parasites are characterized by an enormous *fertility*. For instance, the human
roundworm *Ascaris lumbricoides* is said to lay eggs at the
rate of 1,500 a day. The chain of segments (*strobila*) found in
tapeworms is another similar adaptation, for in the adult, as
new segments are budded off from the head region, old ones
full of fertilized eggs are shed into the gut of the host from
behind.

Hermaphroditism and self-fertilization are also common
among endoparasites, both tending to increase the chance of
producing large numbers of potential young.

Among such forms, direct transmission of the parasite from

host to host seldom occurs. Even in parasites such as the protozoan *Monocystis* which inhabits the seminal vesicles of earthworms, transference does not occur with the spermatozoa during the process of copulation as might be supposed. Infection appears to take place directly from the soil, dispersal of the parasite presumably being achieved by predators on worms such as birds. We have seen how species such as the fluke *Distomum macrostomum* employ a secondary host or vector (the snail) to transmit its larval stage. Such an arrangement is common to many endoparasites which tend to have an *elaborate and complicated life-history*. The tapeworms are notorious in this respect.

Successful internal parasites are called upon to adapt themselves to the narrow and peculiar environments characteristic of the internal structure of their hosts. Although their degree of tolerance varies greatly, all exhibit *specificity* to some extent, that is to say, they are restricted to a single host or group of hosts. For instance the tapeworm *Taenia serrata* is found only in dogs, its larva (*cysticercus*) utilizing rabbits and hares as secondary hosts. Many roundworms are less exacting in their requirements, notably such forms as *Trachinella spiralis* which occurs in man, rats, and pigs. Ectoparasites, being in general far less specialized than endoparasites, often occupy a large range of hosts. Thus the plant roundworm *Heterodera* (Eel-Worm) is known to attack at least 850 wild and cultivated species.

It is often said that parasites exhibit *degeneration* of certain structures present in their free-living or ancestral counterparts. For instance *Sacculina* certainly undergoes profound structural changes as a result of its mode of life. But the dividing line between degeneration and specialization is a very slender one and in endoparasites, just as some organs such as those of locomotion, may be reduced, so others, notably those of reproduction, may be greatly enhanced. Both processes ultimately achieve the same purpose, namely of adapting the organism to its special environment. Furthermore, in many animals such as the parasitic roundworms, tapeworms, and flukes, it is impossible to say whether an organ is degenerate or not, since we know virtually nothing of their ancestors except that they must have had a very simple structure. That such forms exhibit specialization in varying degrees there is, however, no doubt at all.

PARASITE CHAINS

When considering food chains (p. 36), mention was made of the peculiar position arising among parasites, where the pyramid of numbers works in the reverse direction to that for free-living forms. That is to say, starting with a single host the parasites become progressively greater in number and smaller in size. Those which live in or on animals which are themselves parasites are generally called *hyperparasites*. The various associations so far discussed have all consisted of chains with two links. It is not difficult, however, to imagine how a third link might be added when we remember the almost universal occurrence of gut parasites. A typical example would be a small mammal, such as a mouse, which almost invariably harbours a number of ectoparasitic fleas which themselves contain endoparasitic protozoans in their alimentary canals, such as the harmless genus *Leptomonas*. The length of these chains seldom exceeds four links. For instance, among insects, the wood wasp (*Sirex*) bores with its long ovipositor into the wood of trees. At the end of the tunnel the eggs are laid, and when the young larvae hatch they do serious damage to the timber by further tunnelling. However, the Ichneumon *Rhyssa* is of value to man from an economic point of view, since it lays its eggs in the body of the *Sirex* larva where they develop parasitically, eventually killing the host. Finally, if we include the gut parasites of *Rhyssa* such as Protozoa, we have the chain, tree—wood-wasp—ichneumon—Protozoa (see Fig. 17).

It will be seen that at one end of the series is a plant. This is, of course, inevitable in all food chains no matter whether the animals concerned are parasites or free-living.

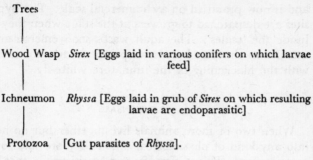

Fig. 17.—A typical parasite chain.

BIOLOGICAL CONTROL

The detailed study of parasite chains has resulted in discoveries of great value to man; for in certain circumstances it has been found possible to bring about the extermination of agricultural and other pests by the artificial introduction of their hyperparasites. This is known as *biological control*. One of the greatest difficulties to be overcome in the successful application of such a method is the fact that outbreaks of destruction by a parasite frequently occur in areas where a successful hyperparasite does not thrive, or where its own predators or parasites are particularly numerous. None the less, on occasions biological control has proved a conspicuous success, particularly in such countries as America, New Zealand, and Fiji (references to these will be found in the Bibliography). In Britain examples are rather few, the most remarkable being the artificial control of the greenhouse white-fly *Trialeurodes vaporariorum*. This insect is a pest of cucumbers, tomatoes, and many other plants grown under glass, and was formerly controlled by fumigation which was both costly and dangerous. The minute chalcid wasp *Encarsia formosa* is a parasite of the immature white-fly ('scales') in which it lays its eggs. Those flies which are parasitized soon show up distinctly by turning black and eventually die. Artificial control by *Encarsia* was first tried successfully in 1926, since when it has been widely used and is now practised on a commercial scale. The hyperparasites are despatched to growers at the stage when they are still inside the 'scales'. The adult wasps soon emerge and their attacks on the pest become apparent in two to three weeks with the blackening of the immature white-fly.

COMMENSALS

When two or more animals live together but do not enter into any kind of physiological union they are said to exhibit *commensalism*. This differs from parasitism in that neither partner exists on the living material of the other, nor at its expense. Sometimes the advantage gained from the relationship is one-sided, while at others both partners profit, the chief benefits from such an association being protection and an abundant and easily obtainable food supply. Commensalism further differs from parasitism in being less intimate, that is to say, the partners are not irrevocably committed to exist together but each is generally (but not always) capable of leading a free-living existence. A parasite, on the other hand, is always dependent on its host at some stage in its life-history.

Commensalism is rare among vertebrates and in Britain does not occur at all. Numerous examples are known, however, among invertebrates, one of the most familiar being that of the Hermit Crab (*Eupagurus bernhardus*) whose soft abdominal region renders it particularly liable to attack by predators. For this reason it is almost invariably found with its tail housed in an empty gastropod shell. A number of different species are selected, the adult generally preferring that of the Whelk (*Buccinum undatum*). This, of course, is not commensalism, for a shell cannot be occupied with the living mollusc inside it. But the opportunity for protection, transport, and food supply is frequently seized by a number of other species, the commonest being coelenterates, in particular the hydroids *Hydractinia* and *Calliactis* which are often found encrusting the whorls of the shell. Other frequent occupants include a variety of polychaete worms such as *Nereis fucata*. The advantages of this association are by no means one-sided, for the crab also enjoys considerable protection from predators as a result of the camouflage provided by the coelenterates on its shell. As far as is known it derives no benefit from the polychaete worms inside, the association being purely to their advantage. One of the most beautiful terrestrial examples of commensalism is provided by the Large Blue Butterfly (*Maculinea arion*). The eggs are laid on Wild Thyme (*Thymus serpyllum*) and the

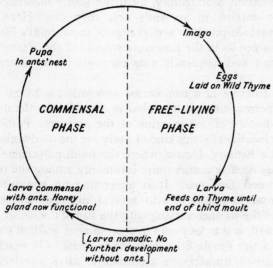

Fig. 18.—Life-cycle of the Large Blue Butterfly (*Maculinea arion*).

larvae feed on the flowers of the plant until the end of the third moult, a period lasting some twenty days. By this stage a honey gland situated on the 7th abdominal segment has developed and started to become active, secreting drops of sweet fluid which is highly attractive to ants. The larva now ceases feeding, leaves the food plant and starts wandering aimlessly about. If it happens to meet an ant, the latter at once takes considerable interest in it, and stroking the honey gland with its legs and antennae drinks the sweet secretion which exudes from it. Soon the ant seizes the larva in its jaws and carries it to its nest where further development takes place. For the next six weeks it feeds on the young ant larvae after which it hibernates for the winter, tended by the workers. In spring it feeds again on ant larvae, subsequently pupating in the ants' nest whence it emerges as the adult butterfly about three weeks later (see Fig. 18). The life-cycle is peculiar in combining the features of a parasite and a commensal. Furthermore, the association is obligatory, for if the young butterfly larvae are not carried to an ant's nest they die. Here, then, commensalism provides a vital step in the animal's life-cycle. This was not so in the previous example of the Hermit Crab which can and frequently does survive with no commensals at all.

The structure of a commensal association is by no means always permanent, but may change according to the stages in the life-history of one or other of the partners. Particularly suitable localities for this kind of study are the mudbanks of the Salcombe Estuary, Devon, where the small polychaete worm *Harmothoë lunulata* occurs quite commonly among the roots of the seaweed *Laminaria*. It is interesting on account of its commensal associations with several different species, the nature of the partner varying with the size of the worm. Thus when small, it is to be found in a prominent position near the mouth of the Brittle Star *Acrocnida brachiata*. On reaching a larger size it transfers its attention to an echinoderm, the Sea Cucumber *Labidoplax*. At a later stage still it is found inhabiting the burrows of other polychaetes such as *Amphitrite*. As far as we know, the benefits conferred by this partnership are entirely one-sided and in favour of *Harmothoë*.

SYMBIONTS

When two organisms live together in close physiological union for their mutual benefit they are known as *symbionts*, the condition being called symbiosis. This kind of partnership differs from commensalism in three important respects.

(i) The relationship between the partners is much more intimate.

(ii) The association is obligatory.

(iii) The advantages resulting are generally mutual.

Some of the best-known symbiotic associations occur between animals and plants; for instance, the freshwater coelenterate *Chlorohydra viridissima* (formerly *Hydra viridis*) harbours in its endoderm cells numerous small unicellular green algae

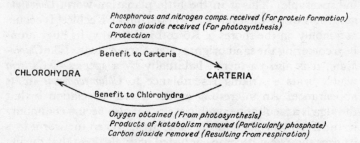

Fig. 19.—The symbiotic relationship between the coelenterate *Chlorohydra viridissima* and the green alga *Carteria*.

of the genus *Carteria*. These are sometimes known as zoo-chlorellae, and are responsible for the animal's green appearance. The animal benefits from this association in that it obtains a ready supply of oxygen evolved as a result of photosynthesis by the algae. Furthermore, being carnivorous, *Chlorohydra* forms considerable quantities of phosphate and nitrogenous substances as a result of the katabolism of animal protein. It has been shown that the algae assist in the absorption of these substances (particularly phosphates) thus acting as auxiliary excretory organs. Such compounds are utilized by *Carteria* to form protein by combination with the carbohydrate which it synthesizes. In this respect it receives further assistance from *Chlorohydra* in the form of a plentiful supply of carbon dioxide liberated as a result of respiration (see Fig. 19). This form of symbiosis appears to be widespread among coelenterates, for some of the reef-building corals of Australia are frequently found to house similar algae which presumably

serve much the same function as those of *Chlorohydra*. They
are often brown in colour on account of the presence of the pigment xanthophyll, and are therefore known as zooxanthellae.

Whether the presence of zoochlorellae in *Chlorohydra* is
essential for the life of the animal it is difficult to say. They are
certainly absent from other closely allied species such as the
brown *H. fusca*.

In one instance at least their presence has been shown to be
indispensable. This is in the little planarian worm *Convoluta
roscoffensis* whose life-cycle was worked out by Keeble.[1] It occurs
commonly on the shores of Roscoff in Brittany, its huge numbers colouring the sand bright green in some areas. Like *Chlorohydra*, it is also partnered habitually by a species of *Carteria*
which bears a striking resemblance to *Chlamydomonas* in its
appearance. An interesting aspect of this association is that
the alga is a facultative symbiont since it also occurs commonly
in the free-living state in the same area. When the worm lays
its eggs they soon become encrusted with algae, so that during
the early larval stage the animal invariably ingests a few while
feeding. These soon multiply giving *Convoluta* its characteristic
quota of green tissue which is apparently essential to its
existence. If a worm is kept uninfected in sterile water, so
that the development of algae cannot occur, it fails to grow and
soon dies. While *Convoluta* is still growing, its symbionts benefit in much the same way as those found in *Chlorohydra*, the
animal being a typical holozoic feeder. But once it has attained
maturity and reproduction has taken place, a remarkable
change occurs. The symbiotic balance appears to become
upset and the worm digests the whole of its complement of
algae, becoming incapable of feeding in any other way. Once
exhausted, the stock cannot be replenished, the inevitable result
being death due to starvation! Thus the partnership starts as
symbiotic but ends as parasitic, the change-over occurring
when the host attains maturity.

Symbiotic associations do not only occur between animals
and plants. Many wood-eating insects for instance, harbour

[1] See Keeble, F. (1910), *Plant Animals*; Cambridge.

numerous protozoans in their alimentary canal. Cleveland has shown that the gut of termites contains flagellates without which the digestion of cellulose, a major constituent of the food, cannot be carried on. It is possible to kill these by heat or starvation of the insect without injury to the host. Termites thus 'defaunated' die within 10 to 20 days if fed on their normal diet, but once reinfested with flagellates, they are again capable of continuing their ordinary existence. It has also been demonstrated that termites can flourish on a nitrogen-free diet so long as protozoa are present, which suggests that they may also be capable of nitrogen fixation or the synthesis of protein from carbohydrate. Presumably the remains of the many protozoans which die inside their host must contribute considerably to its nitrogen supply.

An analogous situation is found in herbivorous mammals where symbiotic bacteria housed in the caecum of rabbits and the rumen of cattle play an important part in cellulose digestion.

THE EVOLUTION OF SPECIAL ASSOCIATIONS

The association between animals and other organisms can be seen to range from a free-living existence on the one hand to extreme parasitism on the other. Between these two limits are a large number of intermediate phases which grade imperceptibly one into another. From a study of such a series it is possible to form at least a tentative idea of the way in which the various kinds of association described in this chapter might have come about. In the first place, from the diversity of the animals involved and their widely differing habitats, it is clear that there can be no question of parallel evolution. The various parasitic associations, for instance, must have been evolved independently and at very different times.

We can imagine the first evolutionary step as being towards the epizoic condition, taken presumably in response to the need for protection and possibly dispersal. From this it is but a short advance towards the more intimate commensalism found in the Hermit Crab. We have seen in the life-cycle of the Large Blue Butterfly how such a partnership can readily change to parasitism, and there is little doubt that a similar step must have occurred many times in evolutionary history. It is unlikely that commensalism would have given rise to symbiosis, for, as we have seen, one symbiont is always a minute organism. These, as far as we know, do not form commensal associations, and it is therefore reasonable to suppose that symbiosis probably evolved independently of commensalism. Again, it is equally probable that commensals and symbionts have originated by various stages directly from free-living forms. The possible courses of evolution might thus be represented as follows:

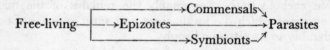

CHAPTER V

CHARACTERISTICS OF LAND COMMUNITIES

THE NATURE OF THE ENVIRONMENT

THE environment in which an animal lives represents a complicated balance of a large number of ecological factors. We have seen in Chapter II how these are in a constant state of change resulting in environmental variation.

Now the unstable conditions to which land animals are exposed often produce great effects upon them, and it is the object of this chapter to consider these in some detail. For the sake of convenience, the various ecological factors concerned will be considered under two headings:

(*a*) Climatic factors; temperature, light, humidity, etc.

(*b*) Biotic factors; those which are the direct outcome of the activities of the animals themselves, such as living space and food supply.

The extent of our knowledge in this field is in many respects scanty, and there are thus innumerable opportunities for useful contributions to be made at an elementary level.

CLIMATIC FACTORS

Land animals are often called upon to withstand far greater extremes of climatic change than their aquatic counterparts. This applies particularly to fluctuations in temperature, light, and humidity which vary with a more or less regular periodicity resulting from seasonal and diurnal change.

TEMPERATURE

In order to lead an active existence, an animal must maintain its body temperature at a sufficiently high level for the various metabolic processes to continue at an optimum rate. It must, therefore, either produce sufficient heat itself by respiration or obtain the balance necessary from its surroundings. Animals are said to be warm-blooded (*homiothermous*) if their temperature is maintained constantly above that of their environment; cold-blooded (*poikilothermous*) if it varies with that of the atmosphere. As this cools, the activity of poikilothermous forms gradually declines until they must either hibernate or die.

Some cold-blooded animals are capable of a certain degree of temperature control. This may be achieved by muscular activity such as occurs in the Python which, when coiled round its eggs, is able to raise their temperature above that of the surroundings for a short time. Others adopt a gregarious behaviour in cold weather such as the larvae of the Lackey Moth. Social insects like the Honey Bee are particularly well adapted for this method of temperature control. During periods of excessive warmth the workers fan with their wings to reduce the temperature in the hive, while in cold weather the bees cluster together thus reducing overall heat loss to a minimum. As we would expect, individual bees are typically poikilothermous.

In all cold-blooded animals, and many of the smaller warm-blooded ones as well, a prolonged fall in temperature results in an unavoidable reduction in activity and eventual hibernation. In Britain, small mammals such as the Dormouse invariably hibernate from late autumn until the spring. During this time their temperature may drop very considerably to a point at which the heart is only just beating. Many invertebrates avoid the difficulties of hibernation by passing the winter in the egg stage.

The effect of variations in temperature on the metabolic rate of some cold-blooded animals is remarkably constant. For instance, the rate of chirping in Field Crickets at temperatures below 50°F. is said to be 40 chirps per minute. As the temperature rises the rate increases by between 4 and 4·7 for each °F. Dolbear has pursued this matter further and proposed the formula

$$\text{Temperature (°F.)} = 50 + \frac{N-40}{4},$$

where N is the rate of chirping per minute.

5. MIMICRY IN BRITISH INSECTS WITH BLACK AND YELLOW BANDING. ×1½

Above—Wasp (*Vespa vulgaris*); Hornet (*Vespa crabro*)
Below—Hornet Clearwing Moth (*Sesia apiformis*); larva of Cinnabar Moth (*Callimorpha jacobaeae*)

6. POLYMORPHISM AMONG SOME BRITISH ANIMALS WHERE
THE GENETICS ARE KNOWN

Above—Normal (yellow) and *helice* (white) females of
the Clouded Yellow Butterfly (*Colias croceus*)
Below—Three forms of the Brown-lipped Snail (*Cepaea nemoralis*)

TEMPERATURE AND ANIMAL SIZE

Besides influencing structure and behaviour, temperature also plays a big part in determining the size that animals attain in different regions of the world. This is governed largely by the balance between the heat that they lose to the atmosphere and the amount they are able to generate or to absorb from it. Now the surface area of an organism increases as the square of its linear dimensions, while the volume increases as their cube. Hence small animals present a relatively greater surface area than large ones. For this reason, homiothermous forms tend to attain a larger size in cold regions than in hot ones, their relative heat loss being less. The converse is true of poikilothermous forms which reach their maximum size in hot climates. Species like the Pigmy Shrew are thus about the minimum size for a warm-blooded animal in a temperate climate, for if they were much smaller they could not eat sufficient food to keep up their body temperature. Similarly, the enormous reptiles which flourished during the Jurassic era (e.g. *Diplodocus* which weighed about 40 tons[1]) could never have survived if the climate had not been a hot one. When it cooled again, all but the smallest and most active became extinct.

LIGHT

Light influences organisms in two distinct ways. In the first place it may have certain important physiological effects governing some of their vital processes. In the second, its influence may be visual, enabling animals to see or be seen.

One of the most important influences of light on animals is an indirect one, namely as an essential requirement for the growth of green plants which form the basis of all food chains.

Another way in which it is probable that light plays a vital part, at any rate among mammals, is in the formation of such substances as Vitamin D (calciferol) by action of its ultra-violet component on the ergosterol contained in the body.

[1] It is worth noting that no great animal of the past ever attained the size of the largest whales of to-day.

This is of great importance, particularly in young animals, since it regulates the quantities of calcium and phosphorus absorbed into the body, and hence the development of all skeletal tissues. Only small quantities of this vitamin are found in the food of animals, and it therefore seems probable that the greater part of their needs must be met by synthesis in this way.

Illumination also plays a vital part among animals in promoting recognition, concealment, protection, and deceit. Different species react to it in greatly varying ways. Nocturnal forms in general tend to avoid it, while some diurnal animals are also shade loving. The great majority, no matter what their habitat may be, have evolved external colours which often play a significant part in their lives.

SIGNIFICANCE OF ANIMAL COLOURS. CRYPTIC (CONCEALING) COLOURS

Many animals appear to match their environment in a general way without assuming any particular colour-tone or pattern to render them less conspicuous in some circumstances than in others. This is sometimes called *general procrypsis* and occurs commonly in the animal kingdom. Among our mammals, the various rodents such as rats, mice, and rabbits all have colours which roughly resemble the great variety of circumstances in which they live. Invertebrates too provide innumerable examples, such as the grasshopper, which is often almost invisible in its surroundings. The extent to which such coloration is developed depends on a variety of factors. In the first place, the variability of the animal concerned plays a large part in determining the success with which it is able to adapt itself to its surroundings when these are varied. In species with a wide and continuous distribution, the conditions will frequently change considerably throughout their range. Such animals can probably do little more than attain general procrypsis. Predators must also play a predominant part in influencing the colours of their prey, for concealment from sight will obviously be of little use against animals hunting by sound and smell. Furthermore, the efficiency of vision, both of black and white, and colour, varies greatly in different species. This is shown by the fact that the optical effects employed in many protective devices by animals living in widely differing habitats do not depend on colour perception at all, but rather on modifications of tone and the skilful use of light, shade, and pattern (see Fig. 20).

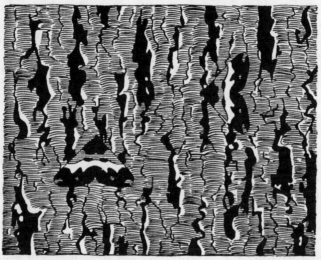

Fig. 20.—The use of pattern as a means of concealment. Note how the insect on the left has become conspicuous due to a lack of conformity of pattern with background.

(*After Cott*)

In certain instances, generally concerned with a rather restricted habitat, animals develop protective colours, shapes, and patterns adapted exclusively to blend with a certain set of conditions. This is known as *special procrypsis*.[1] Among birds, it is particularly common in those species which nest on the ground, a typical example being the Woodcock (see Plate 4, at p. 65), in which the plumage blends admirably with the marsh and woodland surroundings in which it lives.

[1] For quantitative methods of study see, Dowdeswell, W. H. (1959), *Practical Animal Ecology*; Methuen.

When considering the advantages gained by the many kinds of cryptic resemblance found in animals, it is important to remember their purely relative nature. Even with the most elaborate means of concealment, an animal is never completely immune from attack.[1] But if by such means it succeeds in achieving say only a 1 per cent advantage over its competitors, it will have made a big evolutionary step forward. In fact, the advantage so gained in nature will seldom, if ever, be as great as this.

On occasions, cryptic coloration confers both visual and physiological advantages. For instance, the white coat of arctic mammals serves both as camouflage and a means of reducing heat loss. An example of this kind in Britain has already been described in the Mottled Beauty Moth (*Cleora repandata*) on p. 28.

COLOUR CHANGE

Many animals, both vertebrate and invertebrate, possess pigment cells (chromatophores) in their skin, and are capable of changing their colour to varying extents to match different backgrounds. For information on the mechanisms involved suitable references are given in the Bibliography. In some species colour change is under nervous control, in others hormones are concerned in producing it, and in some again, a combination of both occurs; while in many forms the mechanism responsible for it is still unknown. Numerous instances are known among amphibians such as frogs and toads where humidity and temperature influence colour as well as a changing background, while among reptiles, the example of the Chameleon is well known. Invertebrates also exhibit considerable changes, but these have chiefly been studied in aquatic species.

APOSEMATIC (WARNING) COLOURS

Some animals utilize bright colours such as red and yellow, also characteristic patterns which, far from concealing them,

[1] Moreover, in order to be effective, coloration must be closely allied to behaviour, e.g. the ability to remain motionless once a cryptic attitude has been adopted.

tend to make them more conspicuous. Such coloration is known as *aposematic*, and its exponents are almost always found to possess some potent mechanism of defence such as a bite, sting, or unpleasant taste. Their bright colours thus serve as a means of advertisement, warning intending predators to leave them alone. In a few instances, species which are not distasteful have evolved an appearance resembling those that are. These are known as mimics and will be considered separately (see p. 87).

Warning is sometimes achieved by means other than colour and pattern, such as movement, as is found in the larva of the Puss Moth (*Cerura vinula*) which extrudes two whip-like processes from horns at the posterior end of the body, or sound as in the Rattlesnake, or smell as in the Hedgehog.

In some insects such as the larva of the Cinnabar Moth (*Callimorpha jacobaeae*), with its characteristic black and yellow-banded body, warning is of a permanent nature (see Plate 5). In others, this is confined to periods of emergency such as in the common Porcupine (*Hystrix cristata*) which, although nocturnal, is rendered conspicuous by the whiteness of its quills when these are erected. Sometimes both cryptic and aposematic colours are used together. The Scarlet Tiger Moth (*Panaxia dominula*) normally rests showing the spotted forewings only, and is beautifully concealed. If disturbed, however, it immediately exposes the warning coloration of the scarlet hind-wings, and remains displaying them (if the weather is too dull to fly).

Proof of the distastefulness of animals with warning colours is not easy to establish, even with carefully controlled experiments, owing to the small magnitude of the selective advantages involved. However, extensive observations have now been carried out, particularly with monkeys and birds, which confirm beyond doubt that among insects at least, aposematism and unpleasant taste are closely related. The extent to which predators are capable to discriminating between one food and another has also been tested, not only in monkeys and birds, but also among reptiles and amphibians. Again it seems clear that a high degree of preference does in fact exist in these and no doubt other groups as well.

FLASH COLOURS

In some animals with typically cryptic coloration, parts of the body are either brightly coloured or able to be made conspicuous in some other way. Observation has shown that such areas are normally kept covered and only occasionally shown. They cannot therefore be classed as aposematic structures and, as far as is known, none of the animals possessing them provides any evidence of being distasteful. The only occasions on which such colours are exposed are when the animal is about to move, when they presumably serve to distract or confuse potential predators in the vicinity. Hence they are known as *flash colours*. The Red and Yellow Underwing Moths employ this device, the brilliant hind-wings being hidden by the cryptically coloured front pair. The Scarlet Tiger Moth on the other hand, being apparently aposematic, often rests with the red hind-wings exposed. Among birds too, the white central tail feathers of the Wheatear, which are normally hidden, probably serve the same purpose.

EPIGAMIC (BREEDING) COLOURS

Another kind of coloration relying for its effectiveness on advertisement is that connected with breeding. This is known as *epigamic*, and frequently serves as a means by which one sex stimulates the other to pairing and copulation.

The display of such colours is almost always accompanied by characteristic movements, attitudes, and noises. They are particularly well known among birds where the male is generally the more gaudy, although in some such as the Phalarope the situation is reversed. Typical examples of epigamic colours are the plumage of the male Peacock and Argus Pheasant. Among our own birds, many species such as the male Mallard and Bullfinch exhibit this characteristic, the breeding plumage tending to be brighter than that assumed at other times of the year. In these forms the female is generally cryptic in order to match her surroundings while she sits on the nest. Courtship colours also occur to a lesser extent in many other groups of animals, particularly among reptiles, amphibians, fishes, and insects.

MIMICRY

The success of aposematic colours can be said to depend on three main requirements:

(i) The development of a striking appearance.

(ii) The association of that appearance with distastefulness in the mind of a predator.

(iii) The ability of potential predators to recognize individuals employing such colours, and to learn by experience to avoid them.

Now observation in the field, particularly of insects, has shown that in certain circumstances one of two things may occasionally happen. Sometimes members of a species which is known to be palatable and preyed upon regularly, come to resemble in a remarkable way one which is unpalatable and possessing warning colours. Such a situation involving an element of deceit was first described by the great naturalist Bates and is thus generally known as *Batesian mimicry*. On theoretical grounds, the first essential of such an association where false warning colours are used by one species (mimic), is that it should remain comparatively rare by comparison with the one it resembles (model). This is found to be so in nature, for the more common the mimic becomes, so the more worth while it will be for a predator such as a bird to take a chance in the hope of selecting the edible form. In Britain, a typical instance is found among Clearwing Moths (Sesiidae) some of which mimic various wasps, and other stinging insects (Hymenoptera) with black and yellow banding on the abdomen (see Plate 5, at p. 80).

A second kind of mimicry is sometimes found in which two or more well-protected aposematic species converge in evolution towards a similar pattern and colour. There is no deceit here, but the arrangement appears to have been evolved purely as an economic measure to reduce the overall death-rate resulting from trial and error by predators. The existence of such an association was first shown by the German biologist Müller, and this kind of mimicry is therefore generally called *Müllerian mimicry*.

The distinction between the two kinds of mimicry is often not clear cut, for the term aposematism is purely a relative one, and it is therefore often difficult to determine precisely which species are well protected and which are not. Modern knowledge tends to suggest that the majority of mimetic resemblances observed in the field are Müllerian in character. This is what we would expect, bearing in mind that the Batesian mimic must be rare by comparison with its model. It often overcomes this limitation, however, by being polymorphic and having a number of models.

In Britain, Müllerian mimicry is regarded as a rare occurrence. This is no doubt due to a variety of causes, not the least of which is a lack of the necessary observations. Here is a fruitful field for the amateur entomologist. It is known in at least seven species of wasps of the genus *Vespa*, all of which have the typical black and yellow-banded body. Similar colours are found in many other wasps, several bumble bees, saw-flies, hover-flies and beetles, also the larva of the common Cinnabar moth—widely differing species which seem to have 'clubbed together', so to speak, to assume a common warning appearance (see Plate 5, at p. 80).

The study of mimicry is a vast subject (see Bibliography for references), which is further complicated by the fact that most of the instances studied in detail have been confined to insects (particularly butterflies) which are of foreign origin. In conclusion, the main conditions necessary for the development of mimetic resemblances and the biological principles involved may be summarized as follows:

(*a*) Mimics are nearly always found in close association with their models. This is particularly necessary for Batesian mimics where an element of deceit is involved.

(*b*) Batesian mimicry necessitates a precise and detailed

resemblance to the model, whereas for Müllerian mimics, although a high degree of similarity is also desirable, even a superficial resemblance will be an advantage in avoiding undue wastage by predators.

(c) Mimetic resemblance involves not only colours, but often shape and habits as well.

(d) The whole of mimicry is purely superficial, and as such cannot be explained on the basis of parallel evolution or parallel mutation due to a common environment. The remarkable resemblances found among some species of African butterflies have often been achieved by entirely different means. For instance, the chemical composition of the pigments utilized by some models and mimics have been shown to be totally unrelated to one another.

(e) The genetics of some mimetic associations are now known. For example in the oriental swallow-tail butterfly *Papilio polytes*, in which the male is non-mimetic, the female is polymorphic, assuming three different forms, two of which are mimics of other swallow-tails. A single genetic factor, dominant in effect, can convert the male-like form *cyrus* into the mimetic *polytes*. Another changes *polytes* to the second mimetic form *romulus*, but only if the first (*polytes*) factor is also present with which it interacts. This necessarily leads to an approach to a 2 : 1 instead of the expected 3 : 1 ratio, owing to the inevitable accumulation of recessive lethals near the locus of the gene which acts as a switch in determining the alternative forms. In Britain, numerous instances of polymorphism occur in which the genetics are known, but these are not concerned with mimicry. For instance, in the Clouded Yellow Butterfly (*Colias croceus*) (see Plate 6, at p. 81), a single dominant operating only in the female (sex-controlled) converts the normal yellow form into a white variety known as *helice*. One of the advantages conferred by the gene is probably a physiological one enabling the insect to become active at lower temperatures, and therefore to fly both earlier and later in the day than the ordinary female. Again, in the Brown-lipped Snail (*Cepaea nemoralis*) (see Plate 6), a single pair of allelomorphs controls the ground colour of the shell, yellow (left) being recessive to pink (centre). Another pair of genes governs banding (right), that causing its absence (left and centre) being dominant. The two pairs of allelomorphs are also known to be linked. It has recently been shown by Cain and Sheppard that such variation is closely associated with the surroundings in which the snails live. Thus colonies inhabiting open grassland have a relatively high proportion of yellow individuals, while those in, say, beechwoods have a higher percentage with dark red and brown colour. The frequency of banded shells is determined by the uniformity of the background. For instance a beechwood carpet or area of short grass, being uniform, will support a population with a high proportion of unbanded snails, whereas these will be at a lower frequency in a hedgerow in the same vicinity. The three specimens shown in Plate 6 were in fact collected in one locality from (left to right) short turf, beechwood, and mixed deciduous woodland respectively.

Mimicry thus raises numerous interesting problems both for the ecologist and the geneticist, many of which still remain unanswered.[1]

OXYGEN

Air is essential for the life of all animals. This is generally absorbed into the body in solution in the thin film of water covering the region through which gaseous exchange takes place. Since the proportion of oxygen in the atmosphere remains constant at 21 per cent by volume, terrestrial animals are not troubled by the same problems as those living in water where the oxygen content often varies greatly.

Gut-parasites such as tapeworms are faced with the peculiar difficulties of living in an atmosphere where the oxygen content is very low, and it has been shown that some species are capable of respiring anaerobically to a limited degree by breaking

[1] The quantitative aspects of insect mimicry have recently been studied experimentally with conspicuous success. See, Brower, J. V. Z. and L. P. (1958), *Mimicry in Butterflies*; Times Science Review *30*.

down glycogen into carbon dioxide and fatty acids. Their preference is, however, for aerobic respiration, and this must always be possible to some extent on account of the closeness of the parasite to the gut wall which is well supplied with oxygenated blood.

WATER

Water forms the basis of all animal and plant protoplasm. In man, for instance, it accounts for about 59 per cent of his total weight, while in some succulent plants the proportion exceeds 90 per cent. Furthermore, it is essential for all the vital processes of living organisms. It is the basis of body fluids, and provides the liquid medium required for the passage of male gametes in sexual reproduction. In viviparous forms such as mammals the part which it plays has been reduced to a minimum, but in oviparous species notably amphibians and many insects, a free-living aquatic larval stage and sometimes a pupa as well intervene between the egg and the terrestrial adult.

Land animals are able to withstand a lack of water to greatly differing extents. Some, such as the camel, are able to store large supplies, and further augment these by the respiration of fat. Many smaller species are soon killed by desiccation. Others such as ducks and waders live on aquatic organisms, and can therefore never move far away from areas of water.

The water content of the air (humidity) is also important, and is closely linked with the question of temperature control. It is of particular significance in poikilothermous animals, for the greatly increased conduction occurring in a cold, damp atmosphere brings about a more rapid heat loss from the body than in a cold, dry one, a deficiency which a cold-blooded animal may not be able to make good by its own metabolism. In warm climates, temperature reduction is brought about by evaporation of water from the body surface, and so the greater the humidity, the less the amount of heat which will be lost. Homiothermous animals represent living thermostats which are independent of atmospheric conditions. In particular, unlike most poikilothermous forms, they are able to make good excessive heat loss by raising their metabolic rate.

In Britain there is evidence to suggest that the dampness of our winters has played a part in preventing colonization by some cold-blooded migrants. The Pale Clouded Yellow Butterfly (*Colias hyale*) is quite a common summer visitor from the Continent. Since it possesses a hibernating larval stage we might have expected it to become established, at least in southern England; but this has not occurred. Temperature is not a limiting factor as was at one time believed, for larvae have successfully withstood temperatures as low as 19°F. in captivity. It now seems reasonably certain that humidity, coupled with the excessive cooling which it causes, is the primary reason for the failure of this species to survive our winter.

BIOTIC FACTORS. PARASITES AND PREDATORS

The constitution of animal communities always depends to a large extent on the balance achieved between predators and prey or parasites and hosts.

Sometimes colonization of a locality by a new species of animal is prevented by the existence of enemies to which it is not adapted, particularly parasites. A somewhat analogous example to the one discussed in the previous section is that of the Bath White Butterfly (*Pontia daplidice*), a rare migrant from the Continent to southern England. It has been shown that failure to establish itself here has been largely due to its liability to attack by hymenopterous parasites, in particular the Ichneumon *Apanteles glomeratus*. This insect is incidentally of great economic importance, for by attacking the larvae of the Small and Large White Butterflies, it helps to control two agricultural and garden pests.

FOOD

Free-living land animals can be classified on the basis of their feeding habits into carnivores, herbivores, and scavengers.

As already explained (p. 32) these divisions are somewhat arbitrary owing to the varied diet and lack of discrimination in many species.

Carnivores. Carnivorous species are normally those which prey upon other living animals. In a sense, many parasites might be regarded as carnivores since they also feed at other animals' expense. Their position relative to the forms which support them (hosts) is, however, a peculiar one and therefore considered separately (see p. 59).

Some carnivores are directly dependent on plants for at least a portion of their food, such as their Vitamin C requirements. Others obtain these accessory food substances at second hand or even more remotely, depending on whether their prey is itself carnivorous or herbivorous. The diet is nearly always a varied one, and numerous interesting adaptations have been evolved in connection with it. For instance, in mammals such as cats and dogs, the fourth premolar of the upper jaw and the first molar of the lower are modified for tearing flesh—so-called carnassial teeth. Invertebrates also possess many similar structures such as the large mandibles of the ground-beetles (Carabidae), which prey upon a variety of smaller insects. The tiger-beetles (Cicindelidae) are also carnivorous both as adults and larvae, the latter constructing burrows in the soil where they lie in wait for their prey (see Fig. 21).

Herbivores. On land herbivorous species are widespread, and there is hardly a plant which does not constitute the food of some animal. They range in size from large mammals such as the ruminants and rodents to the small larvae of many insects.

The most striking structural adaptations for this kind of diet are to be found in the region of the mouth and alimentary canal. In the larger animals, the teeth may become specialized for gnawing, the incisors being large and chisel-shaped, as in rodents such as the rabbit. Constant friction results in extensive wear of both upper and lower teeth, and these are capable of continuous growth throughout life (hypsodont condition), the pulp cavities remaining open. The premolars and molars are also generally modified for grinding with large ridged surfaces, as in the horse.

Among the smaller herbivores, hard 'jaws' of various kinds have been evolved, such as the rasping radula of the snail and the horny mandibles of most caterpillars.

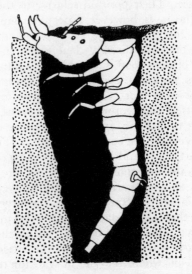

Fig. 21.—Diagram showing the larva of the Tiger-beetle (*Cicindela*) in its burrow waiting for its prey. Note the large mandibles protruding above ground.

(*After Imms*)

Modifications of the alimentary canal for a herbivorous diet are most obvious in the larger animals. The digestion of plant material is slower than that of flesh, and hence the intestine of herbivores is always relatively longer than that of carnivores. This is illustrated by the marked shortening in the gut of the amphibian tadpole at the time of metamorphosis when the diet changes from plants to animals.

All vertebrates, whether herbivorous or not, are incapable of digesting cellulose without external assistance. In rabbits this is provided by resident bacteria which swarm in a blind outpushing of the hind portion of the intestine (the caecum). This structure attains its maximum size in herbivores, but is poorly developed in carnivores, and may be absent altogether, as in some insectivores such as the shrew *Sorex*.

Scavengers. A large assortment of animals feed on the dead remains of other animals and plants. Among the bigger forms scavenging is uncommon, and never serves as the only means of obtaining food. Some notorious examples are the Jackal, also the Bengal Vulture which is protected in India by law, on account of its importance in helping to make good the deficiencies in human sanitation. Many of the smaller animals such as arthropods are scavengers to varying extents, typical instances being the springtails (Collembola) and wood lice.

THE INFLUENCE OF PLANT SUCCESSION ON HERBIVORES

Plants, like animals, live in a changing environment and are constantly being called upon to adapt themselves to new conditions. For instance, in an area of recently cleared woodland, many plants will be found competing with one another for such essentials as light, growing-space, and water. If observation is continued for several years, it will be seen that some species thrive while others decline or perish. Furthermore, there will be an influx of competitors from the surrounding open country, many of which will no doubt establish themselves. In this way the various species succeed one another as new and better-adapted colonists arrive and the nature of the habitat changes. This process is known as *plant succession* and is a feature of all plant communities. It eventually results in the establishment of a kind of equilibrium. The best-adapted plants, frequently the largest and most quickly growing, become predominant, while of the smaller ones, some manage to survive in the shade or protection of the larger, while the remainder are gradually eliminated. When occurring naturally the process is generally slow, but aided by man—as it so often is—it can proceed at a great rate.

Such changes sometimes exert a considerable influence on the animal communities concerned, favouring some and harming others. This extends not only to food supply, with which we are concerned here, but to many other ecological factors as well.

Some of our resident herbivores, by virtue of their varied diet, are able to adapt themselves to the new conditions resulting from plant succession; others cannot. Again, the changed circumstances may favour the arrival of fresh colonists. For instance, Salisbury has described a succession in areas of London where bomb damage during the last war resulted in the total or partial clearance of buildings. Whereas in 1666, after the Great Fire, the London Rocket (*Sisymbrium irio*) was recorded as having flourished among the ruins, after the 1940 bombing, its place was taken by the Rose-bay Willow Herb (*Epilobium angustifolium*), which now abounds in the bombed districts. Its successful colonization has brought about a great increase in the numbers of the Large Elephant Hawk Moth (*Chaerocampa elpenor*) whose larva feeds on the Willow Herb.

But plant succession by no means always favours the resident animal species. Some of the most drastic changes have been brought about by man's thinning or cutting down of woodland. This invariably results in a rapid increase in the amount of undergrowth, particularly bramble, which stifles many of the small plants growing in the shade of the larger trees. Such clearance has almost certainly caused the extermination of the Wood White Butterfly (*Leptidea sinapis*), due to the disappearance of its food plants (various small Leguminosae) in certain localities where it used to be common less than ten years ago.

LIVING SPACE

Most animal communities are extremely sensitive to changes in density which result in over- or undercrowding (see p. 37). Thus the partition of available living space among members of the same and different species occupying identical or kindred

7. SAND AND MUD EXPOSED AT LOW TIDE SHOWING HEAVY COLONIZATION BY THE LUGWORM (*Arenicola marina*) (See also Fig. 24, p. 109)

8. A STEEPLY SLOPING ROCKY SHORE (TEAN. ISLES OF SCILLY)

(See also Fig. 25, p. 111)

ecological niches is often a delicate matter, many factors operating to bring about a final balance. One of the principal of these is food. The feeding area available for each individual is capable of reduction within certain limits as numbers increase, but thereafter colonization of new localities must take place if the food supply is to remain adequate. It is probable that in higher animals a psychological factor also helps to determine the amount of 'elbow room' required by each animal. Birds and insects representing 'higher' and 'lower' animals respectively provide some good instances of the way in which ecological problems of this kind can be solved.

TERRITORY IN BIRDS

In various species of birds behaviour during spring and early summer has been analysed with great care, and has been shown to conform to a definite pattern. Among resident species, the males tend to forsake the winter flocks during early spring about a fortnight in advance of the females. Among migrants there is a similar early arrival of males. These at first lead an isolated and often nomadic existence, but the majority eventually settle down, each within a definite locality from which it seldom moves. Within this area, or *territory* as it is generally known, the male frequently selects a vantage point from which to sing and display. The limits of the territory are actively defended against ecological competitors, both of the same and other species, and fighting often occurs. This generally continues after pairing, frequently with increased vigour. The nest is built within the territory generally near to the male's headquarters, a fact which is of considerable help in finding it. By marking trapped adult birds and nestlings with coloured rings, the limits of the territories of birds inhabiting a particular locality can be mapped with some accuracy. Fig. 22 shows some examples of Robin territories, and the extent to which these vary in size. Lack found that they average about $1\frac{1}{2}$ acres, but there appears to be no constancy either for this species or any other. For instance, those of the Song-thrush in Finland vary from $3\frac{3}{4}$ to $14\frac{3}{4}$ acres.

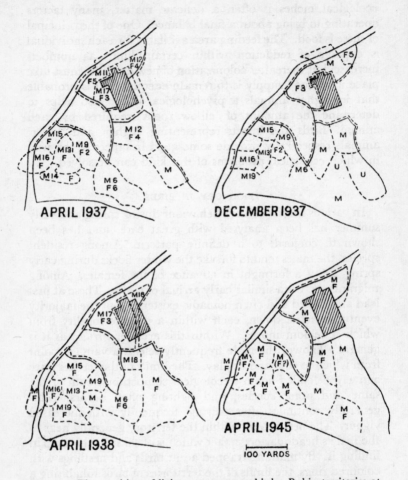

Fig. 22.—The partition of living space among birds. Robin territories at
Dartington. *(After Lack)*

Dotted lines denote the boundaries of territories. The occupied ground is
woodland, orchards, and quarries; the unoccupied areas are mostly fields
and one large building.

M=male; F=female; $\frac{M}{F}$=pair; U=unknown sex. Numbers refer to robins
which stayed long enough to appear on more than one map.

There seems no doubt that the main function of a territory is performed before pairing, in enabling the male to acquire a mate. For this purpose, a bird with a well-defined song centre, and in possession of a good nesting area, will be at a great advantage over one leading a purely nomadic existence. Since defence of the territory frequently continues after pairing has taken place, it has been suggested that it also serves as a convenient feeding centre during nesting. There is considerable disagreement among authorities on this point. Available evidence suggests that its size or situation is independent of the nature or amount of food required, for many species including sea birds, waders, and even passerines, obtain most or all of their food away from their nesting grounds. The fact remains, however, that the majority of territorial species do show a tendency to feed consistently within their territories, and it seems at least possible that this serves not only to reduce fighting and consequent upset of breeding activities, but also to ensure that the minimum time is spent in food collecting. Further, the possession of a common domain may well be of value in helping to keep the pair together. There is also the possibility that territorial behaviour acts as a kind of natural population control by limiting the number of breeding pairs within a particular vicinity. Such a limit certainly exists for all species, beyond which their nesting area can be compressed no farther. Thus Lack found that an aviary 30 feet long and 10 or 20 feet wide was sufficient to accommodate one breeding cock Robin but not two. On such a supposition one would expect to find a considerable number of birds leading a nomadic existence; being those which have either never acquired a territory, or have subsequently been dispossessed of one. Field observations do not appear to support this view. On the contrary, ringing data suggest that once birds have occupied their definitive breeding localities, they seldom move far away except on feeding excursions.

A few birds, such as the Robin in Britain, also exhibit territorial behaviour during the autumn, in as much as single individuals, which are more often males than females, tend to select well-defined areas and fight to maintain them against intruders, from August onwards. This can clearly have no value in breeding, nor does it appear to be concerned with food supply. Territorial fighting is said to become most vigorous during the months of August and September when food is plentiful, and to wane during November and December when supplies are becoming scarce. Furthermore, trespassing by other species is common and rivals for food are not driven off. In such species there seems to be a revival of spring breeding activity the significance of which has yet to be discovered. It is interesting to note that this peculiar behaviour is characteristic of both sexes and not only the male, as in spring. Recent evidence suggests that the secretion of male sex hormone may, in certain instances, also take place in female birds, and moreover, that its artificial injection results in typically male behaviour in some respects. This might perhaps account for the marked autumn territorial instinct exhibited by some females accompanied as it is by active singing.

SOCIAL BEHAVIOUR IN INSECTS

Some insects have adopted the principle of gregariousness rather than that of isolation (as used by territorial birds) in solving their problems of food supply and living space. In many, such as the Lackey Moth (*Malacosoma neustria*), where the larvae are gregarious, the arrangement is only a temporary one during a particular phase in the life-history. But in two orders, the Hymenoptera (wasps, bees, and ants) and the Isoptera (termites), this has been carried to extremes, and is a permanent feature of the animals' life. Thus a remarkable economy has been evolved, whereby certain groups of individuals (castes) have become adapted to perform special duties within the community.

This kind of *social behaviour* is found among wasps of the family Vespidae where egg-laying is restricted to a few females (queens). The remaining females are generally sterile and act as workers. They perform the duties of nest maintenance including the feeding of larvae which hatch from eggs laid by the queen. Late in the summer so-called 'royal cells' are formed in which fertilized eggs are laid, destined to give rise to next year's queens. There is no distinction between the eggs of future queens and workers, the course of their development depending entirely on the nature of the food supply. Those laid in 'royal cells' receive a more nutritious diet from the workers than the remainder. Males arise late in the year from unfertilized eggs by parthenogenesis, and are almost entirely parasitic on the community. Once their task of fertilizing the queens is accomplished they soon die.

In wasps it is interesting to find the beginnings of reciprocal feeding (trophallaxis), a habit widely practised among ants. Thus in return for their carnivorous diet, the young larvae emit a kind of saliva which is eagerly imbibed by the workers.

Only 5 per cent of bees are social, among them the well-known Honey Bee (*Apis mellifica*) about which much has been written (see Bibliography). In general, their social behaviour is similar to wasps except that the worker caste has evolved further and become more highly specialized. The 'royal jelly', supplied by the workers to larvae destined to become queens, contains greater quantities of Vitamin E than that given to the grubs of future workers. That nutrition is responsible for the course of development of a fertilized egg has been proved by transferring larvae from royal to workers' cells and vice versa. Provided the operation is performed within a certain critical period of growth, one can be induced to develop as the other. Trophallaxis does not appear to be practised by bees. Like wasps, the male bees (drones) develop from unfertilized and haploid eggs by parthenogenesis. During spermatogenesis no further reduction division of the chromosomes takes place, the individual resulting from the fusion of a sperm with an egg thus being of the normal diploid kind. A similar situation probably prevails in all species where one sex develops parthenogenetically. One feature of this highly evolved system of reproduction is its 'eugenic' nature, since all disadvantageous recessive genes are exposed to produce their full effects. Drones in which this occurs are largely eliminated during the so-called 'nuptial flight' when the queen takes to the air followed by a swarm of drones, the strongest flier ultimately achieving copulation. Genetic variability is none the less maintained by recombination of factors, the females being diploid.

In ants social behaviour reaches its highest and most complex form. The details vary somewhat among different species, but in all, sexual dimorphism is more marked than in wasps and bees. At various times of the year, nuptial flights occur, the insects showing a marked tendency to fly up hillsides. This is also known among butterflies such as the Small Copper (*Lycaena phlaeas*), and is probably widespread among insects as a whole. It is presumably an adaptation to increase the chances of pairing as the summit is approached. Once fecundated the queen descends, loses her wings and lays eggs in a cavity in the ground. She feeds the young larvae on her saliva and these eventually develop into workers which, as in other social forms, assume responsibility for the maintenance of the nest. In some species the number of different types found among the worker caste is very great, varying from the largest which are termed 'soldiers' on account of their protective and hunting duties, through a number of intermediate stages to the smallest which are the true workers. Between these two extremes more than twenty sub-castes have been described, each performing particular tasks within the community (see Fig. 23). Sometimes certain of the workers may become fertile and capable of pairing with males to lay eggs in the normal way. This usually takes place, either in a species in which the queen caste is absent, or on occasions when a colony loses its queen. But the most remarkable specialization is undoubtedly concerned with feeding, which assumes many different forms, often highly complex. Wheeler has demonstrated the interesting fact that ants seem to exhibit the successive evolutionary stages of hunting, pastoral, and agricultural living in the same way as man is believed to have done. Soldier ants are armed with large mandibles with which they can seize and crush the prey they hunt. An example of pastoral activity has already been described (p. 73), namely the commensal association with larvae of the Large Blue Butterfly (*Maculinea arion*). A similar situation is known to exist between ants and aphids. Agricultural activity is found

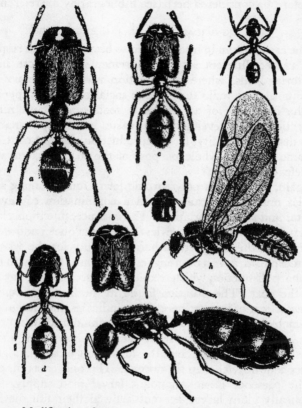

Fig. 23.—Modification of structure in a social insect. Polymorphism in the ant *Pheidole instablilis* magnified. (*a*) soldier; (*b–f*) workers; (*g*) queen after loss of wings; (*h*) male. (*After Wheeler*)

among various species which indulge in collecting and storing plant seeds, also in the cultivation of fungi, quantities of hyphae being transported by young queens when forming new nests. Trophallaxis is widely practised among ants, the larvae providing saliva and also a fatty secretion in return for food supplied by the workers.

Termites ('White ants') are not found in Britain, and will not therefore be considered here (see Bibliography for references).

THE SIGNIFICANCE OF SOCIAL BEHAVIOUR[1]

The caste system in insects seems to have evolved in response to a rather different set of requirements from those in the territorial birds, where reproduction was the primary consideration. The main functions of social behaviour appear to be the insurance of an adequate food supply and mutual protection. The development of castes inevitably demands a high degree of sterility, for if reproduction was not controlled in some way, the whole purpose of the social system would be defeated.

Again, the various polymorphic forms found among social species must have resulted from a combination of environmental and genetic variations. For instance, nutrition plays a vital part in determining the development of queen and worker castes. Yet this alone could hardly account for the whole of polymorphism, as has been suggested by some, bearing in mind the sharp distinction which frequently exists between one form and the next. The situation found in the fruit fly *Drosophila melanogaster* is of interest here, for it indicates one way at least in which the genetic make-up of an animal and its nutrition may interact. In this species it has been shown that a single genetic factor brings about the formation of a 'giant' race, 70 per cent heavier than the normal. This only exerts its effect in the presence of an abundant larval food supply, for if genetically giant larvae are not allowed their full diet they develop into normal flies. Thus one genotype has two quite distinct phenotypes dependent on nutrition. It may well be that some such mechanism in a more highly elaborated form is in operation among the social insects.

---

[1] A great deal has recently been discovered about social behaviour in the honey bee. See, Butler, C. G. (1954). *The World of the Honey Bee*, Collins.

CHAPTER VI

CHARACTERISTICS OF MARINE COMMUNITIES

THE sea and its shores constitute a vast farm of animal life. The variety of habitats which they provide is immense, so also are the numbers of living organisms found within them.

Marine species can conveniently be divided into two groups according to their modes of life:

(*a*) *Pelagic*—those which either swim or float and live in the open sea.

(*b*) *Benthic*—those which live on the bed of the sea and either crawl, burrow, or become attached to various regions of the substratum.

Again, classification may be on a regional basis. Those individuals inhabiting the shore are known as *littorine*, while the remainder can be regarded as *open sea* forms. In this chapter only those animals will be considered which are found on the shore and in the 'shallow sea', that is to say, the zone extending from low-tide mark to a depth of 100 fathoms (600 feet) which marks the edge of the Continental Shelf. In general, the greater the depth the more constant does the fauna, both pelagic and benthic, become. In the littorine zone which is constantly subject to tidal change, a continuous turnover occurs in much of the population as the sea-level rises and falls. In the open sea conditions are more constant. The relative importance of different ecological factors varies greatly in the two zones, and for the purpose of description they are best considered separately.

LITTORINE ZONE

INFLUENCE OF CLIMATIC FACTORS. LIGHT

The shore provides three main kinds of habitat, namely rocks, sand, and mud. Of these the only one influenced to any extent by changes in light intensity is the first. When collecting animals in rock pools it is most noticeable how some invariably expose themselves to light, while others are equally anxious to avoid it. Coelenterates in particular exhibit positive phototaxis and phototropism, for instance the sea anemone *Anemonia sulcata*, which is well protected from predators by the batteries of nematocysts on its tentacles. Vivid colours are frequently a feature of such forms, and these are no doubt largely aposematic (warning colours). But the majority of the inhabitants of rock pools shun light, whether they are protectively coloured or not. Animals such as the Prawn (*Leander serratus*) and the Small Star Fish (*Asterias rubens*) invariably lurk in shady places such as small rock crevices or behind a curtain of seaweed. Littorine animals in general are remarkably sensitive to certain changes in their environment and quickly alter their behaviour accordingly. Periwinkles (*Littorina*) for instance, when exposed at low tide, are positively phototactic and swarm on to the surface of the rocks and seaweeds of the intertidal zone. When submerged once more, their response to the water and waves overcomes that to light and they rapidly retreat to the rocky fissures which afford protection.

Many shore animals have protective colours and patterns which enable them to blend with their surroundings. In the majority, these colours are constant and their usefulness is restricted to a comparatively narrow set of conditions. A few, however, have evolved the power of colour change, and are able to match a variety of backgrounds. In rock pools such behaviour is confined mainly to crustaceans like prawns and shrimps, which possess pigment cells (chromatophores) embedded in their integument. By their expansion and contraction, the animals can become darker or lighter in colour and are hence able to conceal themselves as the illumination varies. It has been shown that this mechanism is controlled by a hormone secreted in the region of the eye. In other decapod Crustacea, such as the Lobster (*Homarus*), the bluish-black colour is permanent, being due to the deposition of α-carotin derived from the food. This incidentally is converted into β-carotin on heating, which accounts for the characteristic red colour of cooked lobsters.

OXYGEN

One of the reasons for the abundance of the littorine fauna is the fact that the sea water in this zone contains much oxygen, on account of its shallowness and constant exposure to the air by the churning action of the waves. The majority of marine animals breathe by gills or lungs, fine folds of skin containing a network of blood-vessels into which dissolved oxygen can penetrate. The body-wall may also play an important part in gaseous exchange, particularly in small animals and larvae. The fundamental distinction between gills and lungs is that, while gills are moistened by water from their external surroundings, lungs are covered by an aqueous layer secreted by the animal itself.

For animals inhabiting rock pools and other regions of the shore where a supply of water is available at low tide, breathing presents little difficulty. But for the remainder, the danger of asphyxiation is considerable, owing to the much slower rate of diffusion of oxygen as a gas than when it is already dissolved in water. This problem is combated in two ways.

(a) Structural changes may take place to enable the respiratory organs to remain in a state of efficiency. In the rocky region of the littorine zone, the gastropod molluscs and crustaceans are the main groups affected. Among the Periwinkles (*Littorina*) for instance, the entrance to and exit from the branchial chambers is guarded by an extension of one of the mantle lobes which serves to minimize water loss when the animal is exposed to the air. This mechanism has been further elaborated in other forms where a completely enclosed tube (branchial siphon) is found. The method employed by the Limpet (*Patella vulgata*) of pressing its shell close to the rock surface is a similar adaptation.

Among the inhabitants of sand and mud (see Plate 7, at p. 96, and Fig. 24) the problem of oxygen supply at low tide is no less acute. Those affected in particular are the worms and bivalve molluscs. Among the polychaetes, the tube-building forms such as *Sabella* employ a variety of mechanisms for ensuring a continuous flow of water through the tube, and hence an adequate oxygen supply. Some are capable of blocking the tube by their tentacles or other means during unfavourable periods. Burrowing forms such as the Lugworm (*Arenicola marina*) have developed clusters of gill filaments projecting from the body-wall, which are well supplied with blood and present a large surface area to the surrounding moist sand.

(*b*) Again, the animals' behaviour may change to conform with their physiological requirements. Thus we should expect to find species best able to withstand exposure to air living far up the shore, while those less well adapted should occur nearer the sea. This, in fact, happens both in animals and plants, and results in the familiar *zonation* (see Plate 8, at p. 97, and Fig. 25), which, although most obvious on the rocky shore, also occurs to some extent in sand and mud as well (see Fig. 24).

Gastropod molluscs such as the periwinkles which inhabit the intertidal zone, show zonation particularly well on account of their varying ability to tolerate exposure. In the driest region (the so-called 'splash zone' which is just above high-tide mark) is found the Small Periwinkle (*Littorina neritoides*) whose range extends so far up the beach as to be out of contact with sea water altogether except during rough weather; even then it is little more than splashed by sea spray. Below this, and overlapping it to some extent, is found the Rough Periwinkle (*Littorina rudis*) which is also capable of withstanding considerable exposure, and may extend for a short distance above high-water mark, but not as far as *L. neritoides*. Below this again is the Flat Periwinkle (*Littorina obtusata*) which inhabits the zone of the large seaweeds such as *Ascophyllum* and *Fucus vesiculosus*, which serve the dual function of providing it with moisture and food. Finally, in the zone nearest the sea is found the Common Periwinkle (*Littorina littorea*), whose habitat overlaps that of *L. obtusata* to a considerable extent, but which is not entirely dependent on the presence of algae

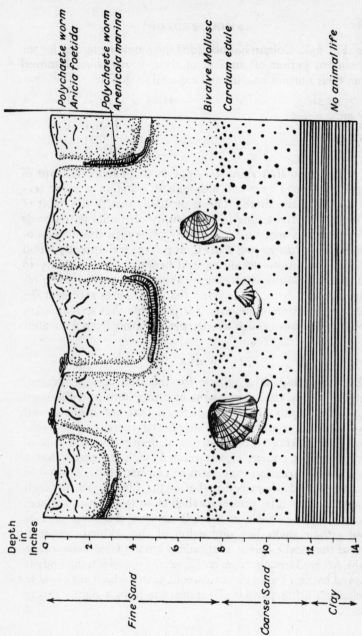

Fig. 24.—Diagram of part of the sandy shore shown in Plate 7 (at p. 96) to illustrate the vertical zonation of animals.

Depth in Inches

0

2

4

6

8

10

12

14

Fine Sand

Coarse Sand

Clay

Polychaete worm
Aricia Foetida

Polychaete worm
Arenicola marina

Bivalve Mollusc
Cardium edule

No animal life

(see Fig. 25). Colgan has obtained the following figures for the maximum period of survival of these forms when removed from their normal habitat and exposed to dry air.

SPECIES	PERIOD OF SURVIVAL IN DRY AIR
Littorina neritoides	42 days
L. rudis	31 days
L. obtusata	6 days
L. littorea	23 days

It will be seen that *L. littorea* appears to be more tolerant of exposure than *L. obtusata* although it occupies a more seaward area of the shore. This is probably due to the habit of *L. obtusata* of remaining in the vicinity of the large seaweeds where there is moisture and plenty of oxygen due to photosynthesis. *L. littorea* (see Plate 9, at p. 112) is frequently found in sandy or muddy localities, and hence a greater ability to withstand exposure is necessary. When interpreting these results it should be borne in mind that the figures represent the *maximum* duration of life, and it is probable that serious harm would result from much shorter periods away from sea water.

WATER

Besides acting as a vehicle for the transport of oxygen, water is also a vital component of protoplasm and the basis of all body fluids. It is thus essential that organisms should take steps to conserve their supplies if there is any likelihood of a shortage. The dangers of desiccation and lack of oxygen are, of course, closely related, with the result that a particular adaptation may seem to combat both. A familiar instance already described is that of the Limpet which, when exposed at low tide, presses its shell close to the rock surface. Bivalve molluscs such as mussels achieve the same end in closing their shells by contraction of the adductor muscle. One of the most efficient adaptations among Crustacea is that of the Acorn Barnacle (*Balanus balanoides*), in which the body is covered by four valve-like calcareous plates which are capable of closing during periods of exposure to form a tightly fitting

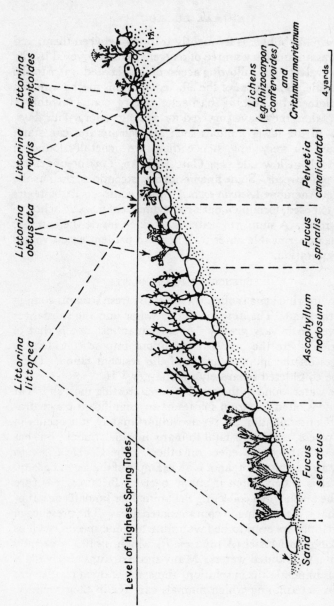

Level of highest Spring Tides

Littorina neritoides

Littorina rudis

Littorina obtusata

Littorina littorea

Lichens (e.g. *Rhizocarpon confervoides*) and *Crithmum maritimum*

Pelvetia canaliculata

Fucus spiralis

Ascophyllum nodosum

Fucus serratus

Sand

4 yards

Fig. 25.—Profile chart of part of the rocky shore shown in Plate 8 (at p. 97) to illustrate the zonation of plants and molluscs (*Littorina*).

roof. An air bubble is frequently trapped between them, and serves as an auxiliary source of oxygen. When covered by the sea the valves open, allowing access of oxygenated water to the gills inside. Some idea of the efficiency of this mechanism can be obtained by keeping barnacles out of contact with sea water, when they have survived for as long as forty-four days.

Few of the lower animals such as coelenterates can stand exposure for very long, hence these are generally found in rock pools at low tide (see Plate 10, at p. 113) or under the cover of seaweeds. Some anemones are exceptions, such as the Beadlet Anemone (*Actinia equina*) which contracts its tentacles when exposed, forming a dark red cylindrical mass attached to moist rocks. A supply of water is retained inside the enteron, and its impermeable outer wall helps to prevent excessive loss by evaporation.

INFLUENCE OF FRESH WATER

The littorine zone is often traversed by fresh streams coming from the land. The amount of this water and the substances dissolved in it vary greatly. A particular instance is that of estuaries where the brackish conditions impose considerable changes on the life and habits of the resident fauna. These will be considered separately in Chapter VII.

The water found in the small streams crossing most shores at low tide is often free from solutes in any significant concentration. Contamination by sewage unfortunately still occurs in some places, and this is fatal to many marine animals, but has curiously little or no effect on others. The Cockle (*Cardium edule*), an inhabitant of sand, is an example of the second group. Since it is widely eaten in many parts of Britain, great care must be taken when collecting the animal for human consumption that it is not living in contaminated areas. The presence of sewage appears even to be favourable to some species, such as the Common Mussel (*Mytilus edulis*) which is often especially common in polluted waters. Many shore streams also contain various mineral salts in solution, and some of them play a vital part in determining which animals can live in their vicinity.

9. COMMON PERIWINKLES (*Littorina littorea*) ATTACHED TO A BOULDER AT LOW TIDE

10. A ROCK POOL FRINGED WITH THE SEAWEEDS

Cystoseira ericoides (dark colour) and *Corallina officinalis*
(lighter colour)

It is well known, for instance, that the presence of calcium compounds is one of the factors governing the permeability of the body tissues. Thus the marine planarian *Procerodes ulvae* is able also to live in brackish conditions, and even in pure fresh water, but only if the necessary calcium salts are present. This is also true of the small annelid *Protodrilus flavocapitatus*.

THE DANGER OF DROWNING

Where land and sea meet, the 'splash zone' just above high-tide mark (see Plate 11, at p. 128) is often heavily colonized by animals, chiefly insects. These breathe air through tracheae and most of them are incapable of surviving for long under water. For such animals there is a real danger of drowning at high tide, particularly during periods of rough weather. Many species such as the fly *Scatophaga littorea*, a common colonist of the dead seaweed which often accumulates in this zone, are agile and able to change their quarters quickly by running or flying. Others, like many freshwater species, have a covering of hairs on various parts of the body which protect the openings of the spiracles. Air bubbles are often entrapped among them, and these serve as an auxiliary oxygen supply when the animal is submerged. The body and hairs are also frequently covered by a waxy secretion which prevents wetting. Many examples of such adaptations are to be found among beetles, such as the common *Aëpus marinus* which is widely distributed along the south coast. This also possesses two large air sacs in the hind region of the body which enable it to float. In some forms the development of hairs has been so efficient that total immersion can occur for several days, as in the common springtail *Lipura maritima* which is frequently seen floating on the surface of rock pools in June and July.

INFLUENCE OF BIOTIC FACTORS. LIVING SPACE

The density of marine communities, particularly of the less mobile species, is no doubt influenced by a great variety of factors. Difficulties in observation and sampling, however, particularly in the deeper water, complicate the investigation of biotic problems of this kind. In the littorine zone there is the added consideration that much of the population changes at each high tide. On occasions, estimates of density have been made for particular species, such as that of the Lugworm (*Arenicola marina*) in the mud-flats of Holy Island, which were found to support more than 82,000 individuals per acre. Whether this large figure is anywhere near the highest density for the animal in that area (or any other) is not known.[1]

FOOD

Food supply plays a vital part in influencing the distribution of marine animals, just as it does in other habitats. For the purpose of convenience the fauna can be divided into herbivores, carnivores, and detritus feeders, although in reality these groups are never clear-cut, and their food chains always closely related (see Fig. 26).

Herbivores. The predominant sea plants are the algae. These range in size from large oar-weeds, like the common *Laminaria digitata*, to the fine filaments of the edible red seaweeds such as *Porphyra laciniata*, commonly known as 'laver'. Other members of the flora are less obvious, the majority being microscopic in size. These include small portions of larger algae broken off from their parent plants by the erosion of the waves, minute unicellular and multicellular algae, and finally diatoms. At high water this vast floating assemblage constitutes the plant element of the plankton. With the retreat of the tide, a considerable quantity of it is deposited over the surface of the shore. Numerous symbiotic associations between algae and fungi are also to be found in the form of lichens, which are particularly noticeable just above high-water mark (see Plate 8 and Fig. 25). A few have succeeded in colonizing the intertidal zone; for instance the common *Lichina pygmaea* forms blackish-green tufts on steep rock faces and has a wide tolerance of exposure to air. In spite of the widespread occurrence of the static seaweeds in the shore zone, it is surprising

[1] For further examples and methods of study see, Dowdeswell, W. H. (1959), *Practical Animal Ecology*; Methuen.

how few animals utilize them directly as food. Those that do so are chiefly gastropod molluscs, such as the Limpet (*Patella*) and Top Shell (*Osilinus*) which rasp at their surface by means of a horny, toothed radula. The great majority of the herbivores in the rocky region prefer to browse on the minute

Ultimate foodstuffs : CO_2 and various dissolved salts.					Putrefactive and fermentative processes ; nitrification, etc.
	Plankton : (Protophyta, Protozoa, and small multicellular animals)	bivalves	carnivorous Gastropods	flat-fish	(man).
		barnacles	ditto	sea-birds.	
		sponges, polyzoa, sea-squirts	Nudibranch molluscs		
		hydroids	Pycnogonids		
		mussels and other bivalves	starfish, sea-birds		
	Fixed seaweeds	sea-urchin	man eats the gonads. ?		
		Helcion pellucidum			
	Organic debris	small crustacea, *e.g.* Amphipods	large crustacea	fish	(man).
		ditto	anemones	Nudibranch molluscs.	
		worms (*Arenicola*, etc.)	fish	aquatic mammals, *e.g.* seals.	

Fig. 26.—The food relationships of some of the plants and animals on the seashore.   (*After Flattely and Walton*)

plants or plant particles deposited from the retreating plankton, many of which are in a state of partial decay by the time they are eaten. This is the commonest kind of feeding among such gastropods as the ubiquitous Periwinkles (*Littorina*). Numerous filter feeders, found mostly among the rocks, also make use of a similar diet. These include the Mussel (*Mytilus*), the Acorn Barnacle (*Balanus balanoides*), and many small tube-building polychaete worms like *Hydroides*, whose calcareous shells are commonly found encrusting rocks, shells, and the fronds of the larger seaweeds in the intertidal zone.

Carnivores. The carnivorous species inhabiting the littorine zone are very numerous, and show great diversity in their foods and methods of feeding. They are largely confined to the rocky region and sandy pools. Rock pools fringed with sea-weeds (see Plate 11, at p. 128) provide some of the best localities for studying these animals in their natural habitat. Among their typical occupants are small fish such as the Gobies, parti-cularly *Gobius paganellus* and *G. minutus*, which prey upon various small Crustacea. These also form part of the food of many of the larger crustaceans such as the crabs and lobsters. Very few of the smaller animals are carnivores, the majority being detritus feeders. Many of the gastropod molluscs are also carnivorous; for instance the Dog Winkle (*Purpura lapillus*) is able to bore through the shells of other molluscs and bar-nacles with its powerful radula. Among echinoderms, the Common Sea-Urchin (*Echinus esculentus*) preys upon other animals, but comparatively few of these are true shore forms. Many of the free-swimming worms are also carnivorous, such as the common red, ribbon-like nemertine *Lineus ruber* and the polychaete *Nereis pelagica* which is frequently found among seaweeds and possesses powerful hooked jaws. All these feed on a great variety of small animals, including crustaceans, other worms and larvae of various kinds. Most of the larger littorine carnivores, particularly the molluscs, are themselves preyed upon by true land animals, particularly birds. No doubt all supplement their diet by varying quantities of plant material.

Detritus feeders. The rotting remains of dead marine organisms play a very important part in the economy of the seas. Breakdown by bacteria and the movement of the water result in the formation of a mass of organic debris on the sea bed which is known as detritus, and some of this is deposited in the littorine zone after every high tide. The exact significance of

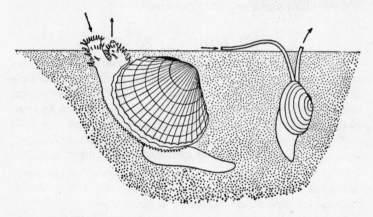

Fig. 27.—Two sand-burrowing bivalve molluscs, the Cockle, *Cardium edule* (left) and *Tellina tenuis* (right). Note the position and shape of the foot, also the action of the siphons through which the water flows (as indicated by arrows).   (*After Yonge*)

detritus as a food for marine animals has yet to be determined, but there is no doubt that it plays an important part in the nutrition of many filter-feeding organisms which are particularly abundant in the sandy and muddy reaches of the shore. It is also widely used by burrowing forms which, like the earthworm on land, extract their food from the mud or sand they swallow. Such species include the Lugworm (*Arenicola marina*) and numerous other polychaetes, also various bivalve molluscs (see Fig. 27). Among the swimming animals, this kind of feeding is practised by such small crustaceans as the amphipod *Gammarus locusta* which is commonly found among seaweed and in the small pools of the intertidal zone.

Detritus is important as a source of food, not only for adult shore animals, but also for their various pelagic larvae, which are not strictly littorine at all, except in so far as they may become temporarily trapped in rock pools and gullies at high tide. The term detritus is used here very loosely, for in addition to rotting organic remains, it always contains quantities of fresh plant particles of various kinds.

SHALLOW SEA ZONE

The area of water between low-tide mark and a depth of 100 fathoms (the edge of the Continental Shelf) represents the shallow sea zone. Within this region ecological factors vary, but not to the same extent as in the littorine zone, on account of the deeper water and reduced effect of the tide.

INFLUENCE OF CLIMATIC FACTORS. LIGHT

In the shallow offshore waters, illumination affects not only the animals themselves, but also the growth of plants on which they are all directly or indirectly dependent.

As in the littorine zone, numerous animal species show marked responses to light, which thus influences their lives to a considerable extent, also those of their predators and prey. Some animals like the small copepod crustacean *Calanus*, tend to avoid the brightest daylight, and to occupy a zone of intermediate light intensity a few feet below the surface of the sea, its depth varying with the brightness of the day. Most bottom-living forms on the other hand avoid light, such as the Angler Fish (*Lophius piscatorius*) which is negatively phototactic.

Nightfall brings about some remarkable changes in the swimming animal community, for the absence of light initiates a general trend towards the surface waters. As the intensity diminishes, each species endeavours to find its optimum illumination, which occurs at an increasingly shallow depth. Such a process may result in vertical movements by some organisms of 50 fathoms or more. With the dawn the reverse process occurs, the animals attaining their maximum depth about noon.

COLORATION

The changing light intensity, together with variations in the nature of the sea bed, provide admirable opportunities for the use of cryptic coloration by bottom-living animals in offshore waters. Among teleost fishes, this is particularly well shown by flat forms like the plaice, sole, and turbot in which the skin contains many chromatophores. These species are capable of matching a variety of backgrounds both uniform in colour and mottled, expansion and contraction of the pigment cells being under nervous control. This can be demonstrated by severing the nerve supply to a portion of the skin which will then fail to change colour with the rest of the body when the animal is exposed to a different background. Experimental illumination from below brings about similar changes in colour, the surface exposed to the maximum light intensity being always the darker. In elasmobranch fishes colour change also occurs, but this is under the control of hormones, as in the dogfish.

Many marine invertebrates tend towards transparency or a bluish coloration. The Chameleon Prawn (*Hippolyte varians*), for instance, is dark-coloured by day and matches the surrounding seaweeds at a depth of 5 to 15 fathoms. At night, complete contraction of its chromatophores (under hormonic control) makes it transparent and blue.

A totally different means of camouflage is used by the Spider Crab (*Macropodia rostratus*), which fixes pieces of seaweed plucked from its surroundings on to its back and legs—a remarkable example of instinctive behaviour (see Fig. 28). If its background is changed, it will remove its former disguise and employ another more appropriate. Other crabs obtain protective resemblance by acquiring a variety of epizoic organisms particularly sponges and coelenterates.

Many species have achieved various degrees of special or general cryptic coloration; but the majority are unable to vary

Fig. 28.—Instinctive behaviour in the Spider Crab (*Macropodia rostratus*), which conceals itself by attaching pieces of seaweed to its back and claws.

(*After Wells, Huxley, and Wells*)

their colours and patterns with those of their background. Aposematic (warning) colours are rare among open-sea forms, either due to insufficient illumination, or because their natural predators would be unable to appreciate them on account of their poor powers of vision.

INFLUENCE OF LIGHT ON FEEDING

Most chemical substances are soluble and generally ionized in sea water. Hunting and the selection of food in marine animals are thus largely achieved by smell, particularly at depths where illumination is much reduced. The eyes of most marine invertebrates are only capable of detecting changes in light intensity. Exceptions are the large molluscs like the cuttle-fishes also the bigger crustaceans, which, although able to form an image, must be very short-sighted. Illumination is important for those fishes which feed during the day-time, such as mackerel; but even these appear to be practically colour-blind and only able to focus on objects a few feet away. In general, the eyes of most fish are adapted to the conditions of dim illumination associated with nocturnal feeding, the retina containing large numbers of rods but few cones.

Light also influences animal feeding by exerting an effect on plant growth. The greatest abundance of marine vegetation is found in the shallow surface waters where the bright illumination enables photosynthesis to take place. As the depth increases and the light fades so the plants become more scarce until, at about 15 fathoms, they disappear altogether. Their place is then taken by static coelenterates, sponges, and other bottom-living animals. A group of plants deserving special mention on account of their economic importance are the microscopic diatoms which form part of the plankton. These provide the food for many of the larvae of such small Crustacea as the copepods, the adults being preyed upon by edible fish like the Herring and Mackerel. The brightness of the weather during the spring months has been shown to be of vital importance in the mackerel fishery, for if the larvae of forms like *Calanus* hatch before the diatoms have become sufficiently numerous, the majority will perish for lack of food, and the numbers of adults will be insufficient to attract mackerel to those areas during May and subsequent months. Temperature and the presence of the necessary dissolved salts, also play an equally important role in the development of diatoms. These aspects will be considered in a later section (see p. 124).

Thus in the open sea, variations in light intensity bring about a marked zonation of the animals and plants, in contrast with the littorine zone, where exposure is the predominant factor concerned. Furthermore, the distribution of the organisms is subject to regular changes in accordance with day and night.

OXYGEN

In offshore waters the amount of dissolved oxygen decreases with increasing depth. Incidentally, variations in temperature and salinity may also influence its concentration, but these factors are seldom significant in the sea around our coasts.

Since the surface of the water is constantly exposed to the air it is generally saturated, but below, a gradient of decreasing oxygen tension tends to develop reaching its minimum on the sea bed. This is offset to a considerable extent by the movement of water set up by the ocean currents, and nearer the surface, by the churning action of the waves during rough weather. In the region of seaweeds, photosynthesis also causes a local increase in oxygen supply.

Such variations no doubt tend to reinforce the effects of changing light intensity (see p. 121). Many species undergo a rhythmical movement towards the surface during the night and away from it during the day in response to fluctuations in illumination. In so doing, the majority will reach the zone of high oxygen content for at least a short period during each 24 hours.

The permanent inhabitants of the sea bed have to make the best of the limited oxygen supplies available, and in general their rate of metabolism is much lower than surface-dwelling species. They are either static, like the sponges and numerous coelenterates, or burrowing, such as many worms and molluscs, or sluggish forms like the various flat-fish.

TEMPERATURE

The sea is subject to distinct variations in temperature, both diurnal and seasonal. Around our coasts, the surface offshore water fluctuates by about 8°C. between summer and winter. As the depth increases these changes become less marked, and at 100 fathoms the temperature during winter is seldom more than 2°C. below that in the summer. In the littorine zone fluctuations between tides may be much more severe, but these are only of relatively short duration.

Marine animals in general are capable of withstanding the normal range of temperature without difficulty. Extremes may, however, prove fatal, as happened for instance in the Cockle (*Cardium edule*) at Loch Fyne Head during the cold winter of 1929. Severe heat may have an adverse effect as was evident in the same species in the Dee estuary during the hot summer of 1933. Some marine animals manage to avoid extremes of cold by regular seasonal movements to deeper water. This is so in many small fish, such as the Gobies, also among some of the Crustacea, notably the Edible Crab (*Cancer pagurus*) and Lobster (*Homarus vulgaris*).

From time to time animal inhabitants of warmer zones are driven towards our shores by the action of ocean currents or storms. Some of the large coelenterates like the Portuguese Man-of-War (*Physalia*) and the much smaller *Velella* occasionally appear in the Scilly Islands and elsewhere. The majority of these perish, but some have managed to establish themselves and a few now provide industries of great economic importance. The Pilchard fishery along the Cornish coasts is a typical example, the species being essentially an inhabitant of southern waters, which has extended its range northwards as far as our south-western seaboard.

An important indirect effect of temperature upon animals is its influence on plant growth. This applies particularly to the development of minute organisms such as the diatoms which form the end-link of so many of the food chains of marine animals.

WATER

The sea is a complex mixture of chemicals many of which are salts in solution. The chief of these are the chlorides of sodium and magnesium, which together account for about 3·1 per cent by weight of the water around our coasts. Other substances occur in much smaller quantities, and traces of the majority of elements have been identified. Also suspended in the water are large quantities of organic particles (detritus) which play an important part in the economy of the sea.

In our offshore waters, variations in salinity are generally so small as to have little or no effect on the animal inhabitants. Exceptions to this are those areas where large quantities of fresh or brackish water flow into the sea from the land, particularly in the vicinity of estuaries. These are considered separately in Chapter VII.

'Trace substances' (compounds occurring in minute concentrations) are no doubt also important in the sea, but our knowledge of them is not comparable with that of their counterparts on land. Evidence of their action is provided by situations such as that found in the small shrimp *Gammarus chevreuxi*. This thrives in brackish conditions near Plymouth, but is quickly killed if transferred to similar water compounded from the Adriatic. The species is able to withstand a wide range of salinity, and its inability to adapt itself must therefore be due to the presence of one or more toxic substances to which it is unaccustomed in its native habitat.

THE NITROGEN CYCLE IN THE SEA

In order to support the vast quantity of marine plants, a constant supply of nitrogen compounds is required. The turn-over of these takes place in a manner very similar to that on land with one important difference, namely that the contributions by man, which play such an ever-increasing role in the soil, are negligible in the sea.

The marine nitrogen cycle also differs from that on land in two other respects:

(i) Organic debris is heavier than sea water and so tends to sink to the bottom.

(ii) During the summer the surface waters down to about 7 fathoms become warmer, and therefore less dense than the water below. Thus during the warm months, a dividing line occurs at about this depth between the upper warm water containing little organic material and the lower cold water with much debris.

Since illumination tends to reach its maximum during summer, the warmer surface waters once denuded of essential salts by the rapidly growing plants are unable to replace them until the winter, when the temperature barrier disappears and the lower fertile water is able to mix once more with the depleted upper zone. This effect is overcome to some extent in rough weather when waves mix the surface waters, but in general it is a constant feature of the summer seas. The influence of such a cycle is most apparent on the plant plankton, which fluctuates in accordance with the fertility of the well illuminated surface waters, reaching its maximum in the spring and autumn (see Fig. 29). It is thus vital that the many herbivorous larvae and adults of small species such as the copepod Crustacea should synchronize their life-cycle with that of the nitrogen supply, if they are to obtain sufficient food.

CURRENT

The strength and direction of sea currents vary considerably at different times of the year. Furthermore, they are not easy to determine accurately even in comparatively shallow water, with the result that our knowledge of their influence

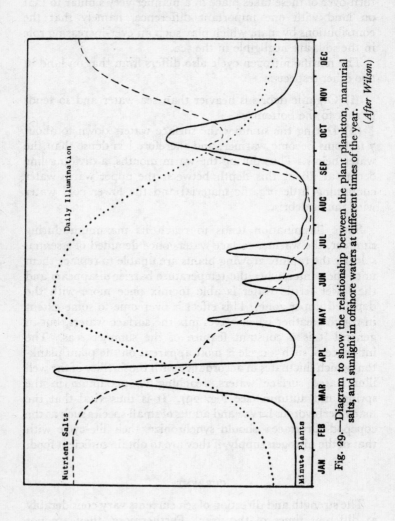

Fig. 29.—Diagram to show the relationship between the plant plankton, manurial salts, and sunlight in offshore waters at different times of the year.

(*After Wilson*)

on marine animals is somewhat scanty. Their principal effects are twofold:

(i) In assisting the dispersal of organisms.
(ii) In governing the distribution of floating food.

Many of the young stages of marine invertebrates possess little or no power of locomotion, for instance the larvae of annelids and crustaceans, also the medusae of coelenterates. Weakly-swimming adults too, like the jellyfish (Scypho-medusae), are dispersed to a large extent by the ocean currents. It is thought that these may also influence the movement of such vertebrates as the Pacific Salmon (*Onchorhynchus*) and other fish, which as a general rule tend to swim against the prevailing current while their eggs and larvae are carried passively with it.

In dispersing floating organisms, the flow of the water obviously plays a large part in influencing the distribution of the animals which feed upon them. This is of great economic importance in such industries as the herring fishery, where the collection and estimation of plankton to determine its composition, density, and direction of movement, is now carried out as a routine procedure.

INFLUENCE OF BIOTIC FACTORS. FOOD

The foods and feeding methods of animals inhabiting the shallow sea are not easy to study. Although well known in some species of economic importance, our knowledge of others is extremely scanty. As in the littorine zone, the fauna can be divided for convenience into carnivores, herbivores, and detritus feeders.

Carnivores. The eggs and larvae of many marine forms are subject to tremendous wastage as a result of the activities of carnivores. To combat this, the fertility of such species is prodigious. For instance, the female Turbot is estimated to produce between five and ten million eggs during the course of its lifetime. The mortality of adult invertebrates is also high, while many small vertebrates are preyed upon by the larger fish, birds, and mammals. The diet of marine species is generally very varied, and often changes considerably as the animals grow older and larger. Thus food chains become exceedingly complex (see Fig. 4, p. 35).

Nearly all fishes are carnivores, the majority seeking their prey by smell. Some, like the Angler Fish (*Lophius piscatorius*), make use of their eyes as well, while a few, notably the Common Sole (*Solea vulgaris*) possess sensory tactile processes which serve as an additional means of detecting food. Among invertebrates, there are many carnivores, some of the largest in British waters being the cephalopod molluscs such as the Common Octopus (*Octopus vulgaris*) and Cuttlefish (*Sepia officinalis*) which feed mainly on crustaceans. Many of the larger gastropod molluscs and Crustacea are carnivores, so also are some echinoderms. For instance the Burrowing Starfish (*Astropecten irregularis*) may sometimes become an economic menace on account of its depredations in oyster-beds and among the small bivalve molluscs which form the principal food of the Plaice. Many of the shallow water annelids, nemertines, planarians, and coelenterates are also carnivores to varying extents.

Herbivores. As on the seashore, comparatively few herbivorous animals are directly dependent on the seaweeds for their food. The majority of adults and all larvae subsist on minute living plant fragments, small algae, and diatoms. Among fish the Grey Mullet (*Mugil chelo*) provides an exception since it frequently feeds on the finer filamentous algae. Apart from a few such species the great majority of herbivores are filter feeders. These include the Oyster (*Ostrea edulis*), and Chinaman's Hat Shell (*Calyptraea chinensis*), among the molluscs, many of the smaller crustaceans such as the copepods, also numerous annelids, coelenterates, and sponges. In most of these it is impossible to make a clear distinction between a detritus and true herbivorous diet, for no doubt they consume both living and dead plant matter.

An interesting and unusual filter feeder is the so-called

11. WHERE LAND AND SEA COMMUNITIES MEET. THE ACCUMULATION OF DEAD SEAWEED IN THE SPLASH ZONE PROVIDES A HABITAT FOR MANY SMALL INSECTS

12. PORTION OF A JETTY PILE SPLIT OPEN TO SHOW LIVING SPECIMENS OF THE SHIPWORM (*Teredo navalis*) IN THEIR BURROWS

Shipworm.   This is really a bivalve mollusc *Teredo navalis*, with a long worm-like body and much reduced shells which serve as a rasping device with which the animal bores into timber to a maximum depth of about 18 inches (see Plate 12). Although feeding mainly on minute plant particles, *Teredo* also derives a certain amount of nourishment from the surrounding wood. At one time a notorious pest of ship hulls, it still inflicts considerable damage on piers and other wooden structures permanently submerged in the sea.

Detritus Feeders. As pointed out in the last section, there is no hard and fast distinction between herbivores and detritus-feeding forms. In the majority of filter feeders, the size of the food particles rather than the nature of their composition determines whether they are selected or not.

In general, detritus feeding is confined to those species which consume quantities of sand and mud, from which they extract substances of nutritive value.   This procedure is characteristic of many burrowing annelids like the polychaete *Aphrodite aculeata*, which is generally to be found in fine sand at a depth of 20 to 30 fathoms. Similar habits occur among some echinoderms, notably the Sea Cucumber (*Holothuria forskali*), and the Sea Urchin (*Echinocardium cordatum*), both of which are typical burrowing species.

CHAPTER VII

CHARACTERISTICS OF ESTUARINE COMMUNITIES

WHERE river and sea waters meet, a brackish zone is formed in which the composition of the water is constantly changing. At high tide there is a period of maximum salinity while at low tide, and in periods of heavy rain, the extent of the freshwater zone is greatly increased. Such fluctuations provide problems for animal colonists not found in any other kind of habitat, and the means by which they are solved merit consideration on their own.

The conditions prevailing in different estuaries vary greatly, depending on topographical and other factors. But certain fundamental features remain common to all, and these invariably demand much the same kind of adaptations by the animal communities concerned.

INFLUENCE OF CLIMATIC FACTORS. WATER

In water where the concentration of dissolved substances is unstable, the resident animals are faced with two distinct problems. In the first place, they have to regulate the amount of fluid which enters or leaves their bodies as the osmotic pressure of the surroundings changes (osmo-regulation). Secondly, they may have to adapt themselves to tolerate the presence (or absence) of certain specific minerals. This resembles the situation found in small freshwater streams as they traverse the shore on their way to the sea (see p. 112). The two problems may be closely related to one another.

OSMO-REGULATION

Many marine animals such as echinoderms, cephalopod molluscs, most coelenterates, and many annelids, are incapable of living in estuaries on account of their limited powers of osmotic control. Such species can only tolerate small osmotic changes and are known as *stenohaline*. Resident forms are always characterized by a wide range of osmotic tolerance (*euryhaline*). The difference is well shown by some of the common molluscs. For instance, such typical shore forms as the Limpet (*Patella vulgata*) and Dog Winkle (*Purpura lapillus*) never penetrate into the estuarine zone which is, however, habitually colonized by the Cockle (*Cardium edule*) and Oyster (*Ostrea edulis*). Both of these, together with many other estuarine species are found to survive in fresh water under experimental conditions for several weeks. Among crustaceans too, the Spider Crab (*Maia*) is confined to rocky and sandy habitats in offshore waters, whereas the Shore Crab (*Carcinus*) is able to penetrate up-river to a considerable distance, almost reaching fresh water. Among annelids, another true brackish form is the polychaete *Nereis diversicolor* which is common in the muddy reaches of many estuaries.

If changes in the internal osmotic pressure ($\triangle i$) are plotted against corresponding variations in external osmotic pressure ($\triangle e$), an interesting comparison can be made of the powers of osmo-regulation in stenohaline and euryhaline forms (see Fig. 30). It will be noted that osmotic pressures are expressed in terms of freezing-point depressions to which they are directly proportional. This indicates clearly why stenohaline species in general cannot colonize estuaries, for their internal osmotic pressure is largely (if not completely) dependent on that of their surroundings.

Sometimes the members of a single genus possess strikingly different salinity requirements. For instance in the amphipod crustacean *Gammarus*, the typical marine species are *G. locusta* and *G. marina* which are unable to extend their range far into estuarine conditions, where they are replaced by such forms as *G. zaddachi* and *G. duebeni*. Spooner has examined the salinity-tolerance of two sub-species of *G. zaddachi* and found the maximum for *G. z. salinus* to lie in the neighbourhood of 3·1 per cent, while that for *G. z. zaddachi* is about 1·5 per cent. He has further shown that *G. z. zaddachi* may frequently penetrate for some distance into permanent fresh water, although it is generally unable to reproduce in such conditions. The typical inland species inhabiting shallow, swiftly flowing rivers and streams is *G. pulex*, which does not stray into brackish water.

Among vertebrates, the majority of marine fish are stenohaline and unable to survive in estuaries. A few exceptions such as the Flounder (*Pleuronectes flesus*) are capable of swimming

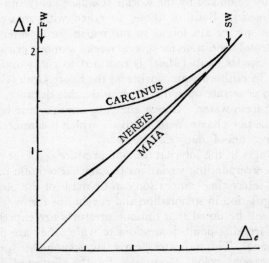

Fig. 30.—Variation of internal osmotic pressure ($\triangle i$) with changes in external osmotic pressure ($\triangle e$) in some aquatic invertebrates. FW=fresh water; SW=sea water.

(*After Baldwin*)

up-river for considerable distances and even of surviving in fresh water. Migratory species like the eel (*Anguilla vulgaris*) spend most of their adult life in rivers, but return to the sea to breed. In these the internal osmotic pressure is approximately one third that of sea water. Osmo-regulation in the eel is achieved by an impermeable outer covering of slime. In the salmon, the scales provide an almost impermeable layer, and the relatively small quantity of excess water entering the body during the animal's river existence is got rid of by the kidneys.

When in the sea, the action of the so-called chloride secretory cells in the gills raises the salinity of the blood approximately to the same concentration as the surrounding medium, thereby avoiding loss of water to the exterior.

Many burrowing forms such as the Lugworm (*Arenicola marina*) do not possess great powers of osmo-regulation but are none the less successful colonists of estuaries. These are able to descend to a sufficient depth for the penetration of water to be comparatively slow, and resulting variations in the environment therefore relatively small. Their range often extends up-river for some distance, and even to areas subject to the maximum changes in salinity between high and low water.

OTHER EFFECTS OF DISSOLVED SUBSTANCES

The presence of various minerals in the water, particularly calcium salts, is known to be of importance in governing the permeability of the body tissues of animals. This in turn is a vital factor in determining the capacity of a species for osmo-regulation. The situation in the planarian *Procerodes ulvae* which sometimes inhabits freshwater streams crossing the littorine zone, has already been considered (see p. 113). Although little is known about them, it seems likely that similar instances must occur among many estuarine forms.

The difference in density of salt and fresh water probably has another important influence on animal colonization, on account of the corresponding changes in buoyancy. Baldwin has pointed out that many floating larvae of marine species which feed on the minute algae and diatoms inhabiting the brightly illuminated surface waters, may well tend to sink to the bottom in less dense fresh water, where they must soon starve.

CURRENT

The rate of flow of the water varies greatly in different estuaries, also in the various zones of any one. It is influenced by a great number of factors, some of the most important being the state of the tide, the amount of water flowing down-river, and the topography of the river mouth. No matter how great their osmotic tolerance, animals will have little chance of establishing themselves as adults unless they are able to withstand the force of the current. Exceptions to this are the burrowing forms which, once submerged, are admirably protected. This is perhaps one reason why species such as the planarian *Procerodes ulvae*, seldom, if ever, penetrate up-river although typically euryhaline.

The same consideration applies even more to young stages such as larvae and nymphs. As a general rule, the free-swimming young of estuarine and freshwater animals tend to remain inside the egg until they have reached a stage at which they can swim against the prevailing currents, or are adapted in other ways to withstand them. This view is supported by the fact that in many species, the eggs of estuarine forms contain a larger supply of yolk than their marine counterparts. For instance, among crustaceans the prawn *Palaemonetes varians* has two sub-species, *microgenitor* which is marine and *macrogenitor*, a freshwater form. The female *microgenitor* lays about 320 eggs a year of mean diameter 0·5 mm., while *macrogenitor* lays only 25 of mean diameter 1·5 mm.

Another action of the current is to stir up the quantities of fine mud collecting in the region of an estuary, most of which is carried down by the river. The water then becomes turbid and the penetration of light is much reduced. This has an adverse effect on many animals, particularly the filter feeders which tend to be choked by the sediment. Furthermore, most aquatic plants are unable to survive under such conditions, so that the food available for herbivores is much reduced.

TEMPERATURE

The constant turn-over in the water of estuaries brings about considerable changes in temperature of comparatively short duration. It is doubtful if these are ever as great as the fluctuations which most littorine animals have to withstand. Marine forms with a narrow temperature tolerance (stenotherms), inhabiting deep waters, may be prevented from colonization by such a barrier, but it seems unlikely that other species, such as all littorine animals, would be excluded on this account.

There is some evidence that in the lower invertebrates such as coelenterates, temperature may play a part in influencing the permeability of the body tissues, and hence the amount of variation in salinity which they can tolerate. It is doubtful, however, if this is a significant factor in the majority of the estuarine fauna.

INFLUENCE OF BIOTIC FACTORS. FOOD

In estuaries, aquatic plants are comparatively scarce. Those which are able to exist there show a distinct zonation according to their ability to tolerate varying salinity. There is an almost total absence of the littorine seaweeds, an exception being the green filamentous alga *Enteromorpha intestinalis* which frequently ranges almost into the freshwater region. The inland mud-flats support a varied and characteristic halophytic flora which provides anchorage, protection, and food for a large number of herbivorous forms, particularly molluscs (see Plate 13, at p. 160). Conspicuous among these plants is the Cord Grass (*Spartina townsendii*), a species unknown outside Britain and now a colonist of many of our south-coast estuaries, also the Sea Rush (*Juncus maritimus*).

The problems facing carnivores are little different from those provided by sea and inland waters. In general, the community enjoys a considerable degree of isolation from aquatic predators on account of their inability to adapt themselves to the changing conditions. On the other hand, estuarine waters are nearly always shallow, which renders their occupants increasingly liable to attack from the air by birds such as gulls.

Among the detritus feeders, numerous burrowing species flourish in estuaries, notable among them being the Lugworm (*Arenicola marina*) which is often found in great numbers and provides a valuable bait for fishermen. The constant erosion by the water of river-beds and the seashore, results in the deposit of large quantities of silt in the estuarine zone, and with it considerable amounts of living and dead plant material. The characteristic mud banks so formed, may either remain permanently submerged, or in time may rise above the water becoming sand dunes and thus no longer capable of supporting aquatic animal life.

CHAPTER VIII

CHARACTERISTICS OF FRESHWATER COMMUNITIES

IT is seldom necessary to look far in order to find a freshwater animal habitat. Naturally occurring rivers, streams, and ponds, or artificial constructions such as canals and ditches all support their own peculiar fauna whose composition and habits vary greatly at different times of the year. Unlike the open sea where conditions remain comparatively constant, the characteristics of fresh water (in the widest sense) are exceedingly variable. So too are the animal species living in it, which makes the study of their ecology all the more interesting.

Owing to their great diversity, it is impracticable in a brief account to subdivide freshwater habitats into various types as is possible in the sea. Suffice it to say that a rough division can be made into static and flowing waters, but even this is by no means absolute.

INFLUENCE OF CLIMATIC FACTORS. TEMPERATURE

In most areas of fresh water except the depths of large lakes, the temperature varies greatly. Such changes, both diurnal and seasonal, play a considerable part in the lives of the animals and plants concerned.

The onset of cold weather brings about a marked reduction in the activity of freshwater animals since they are practically all cold-blooded (poikilothermous). They are then faced with two alternatives:

(i) Of carrying on as they are but at a reduced metabolic rate. This frequently amounts almost to a state of suspended animation.

(ii) Of adopting some special hibernating phase.

Many freshwater fishes, including the Loach (*Cobitis barbatula*) and Minnow (*Phoxinus*), become sluggish during cold weather and tend to move to deeper water where the temperature change is less marked. Among invertebrates, many active aquatic insects like the Whirligig Beetle (*Gyrinus natator*) and the Water Boatmen *Corixa* and *Notonecta*, forsake the surface waters and burrow into the mud for protection during the winter. Others such as the molluscs maintain their normal existence, but at a much reduced rate of activity. In practically all species reproduction ceases during the winter months.

The second alternative is favoured by many of the small insects; these over-winter in an inactive resting stage well able to survive the cold. This may be a burrowing larva as in the midge *Forcipomyia*, or nymph as in many may-flies, e.g. *Ecdyonurus*. Often the winter is passed as an egg protected by a horny case as in the coelenterate *Hydra*. Among Crustacea, the water-fleas such as *Daphnia* and *Simocephalus* can produce special resting eggs which are formed in autumn when the temperature drops. Each female lays one or two such eggs at a time, which are not only thick-walled, but also enclosed in a portion of the maternal skin, which breaks away from the rest when the next moult occurs. The eggs, thus enclosed in a horny sac (ephippium), sink to the bottom where they remain dormant during adverse conditions. During the early autumn females may often be found containing ephippia, and are easily identified in a jar of water by their dark brown appearance.[1]

Freshwater animals are generally able to withstand a wide range of temperature (eurythermous). Fishes are known to survive conditions well below freezing-point, while it is a common occurrence to find frogs existing unharmed at the bottom of frozen ponds. There is no evidence that invertebrates are any less resistant to the cold than vertebrates, provided the concentration and nature of dissolved substances remain favourable.

Most species tend to move towards areas of greater warmth

[1] Under favourable conditions reproduction is entirely parthenogenetic, as many as a hundred eggs being laid at a time.

(positively thermotactic), and with the coming of spring and summer the well illuminated surface waters are soon crowded with animal life. Exceptions are the few forms with a poor tolerance of temperature change (stenotherms) which inhabit the depths of great lakes or other similar localities. Such relict species as the turbellarians *Planaria alpina* and *Polycelis cornuta* which occupy small isolated areas of cold water arising from mountain springs, are remnants of a much more widespread population dating back to glacial times. Both these show well defined negative thermotaxis; no doubt an adaptation to maintain them in the coldest region of their habitat.

Deep Lakes. In most areas of shallow, static water the temperature is relatively uniform. The absence of any permanent gradient from top to bottom can be accounted for by the fairly rapid action of convection currents assisted by the wind. At greater depths, however, marked variations tend to occur and these fluctuate considerably at different times of the year. Since water reaches its maximum density at 4°C., the bottom of a deep lake may well remain almost constantly at this temperature throughout the year and thus become a suitable habitat for stenothermous species, provided the necessary oxygen and food supplies are available. During the coldest part of the winter, the temperature will fall slightly with decreasing depth reaching 0°C. in the surface water. With the onset of warmer conditions, the gradient is gradually reversed by the action of convection currents, although this effect seldom extends deeper than about 60 feet.

LIGHT

Most areas of fresh water are fairly brightly illuminated even at their greatest depth. This is important, for without light the many aquatic plants both large and small, which form the basis of all animal food chains, are unable to survive. In swiftly-flowing streams and rivers little plant or animal plankton will be found. This is not due to a lack of light, but to the action of the current in washing it away.

Illumination and background also exert an important effect on the colours of freshwater animals. While those of the shore and shallow sea display a wide diversity of colour and pattern, also in many instances the power to alter their appearance to a striking degree, their freshwater counterparts are mostly of sombre hues and seldom capable of any appreciable colour change. Such a difference cannot be attributed entirely to the nature of the surroundings in which the animals live, although no doubt inland waters do exhibit greater uniformity than marine habitats. The chief factor concerned here is the nature of the predators and their ability to select their prey by sight. In the sea the larger carnivores, such as fishes and cephalopod molluscs, have comparatively good eyesight and are particularly numerous, hence the development of special cryptic or aposematic colours by potential prey will be of considerable use. In fresh water this necessity does not arise to the same extent, for the majority of invertebrate carnivores are small with relatively poorly developed eyes, and fishes are far fewer in number.

RESPONSES TO LIGHT—PHOTOTAXIS

The presence or absence of light influences the behaviour of freshwater animals to a marked degree. Forms like may-fly nymphs are negatively phototactic and seek the undersides of stones where there is a minimum of light. This response serves not only to protect the animal from predators, but also to enable it to avoid the full force of the current in the swiftly flowing streams where it lives. In many of the water-fleas (Cladocera) such as *Polyphemus*, which forms an important part of the plankton in static water, behaviour varies with the light intensity. Thus they are positively phototactic to weak light but move away from bright illumination. It has been shown that age may influence this light reaction, for young *Daphnia* exhibit strong positive phototaxis while the adults react in the opposite manner. The significance of this is not clear, but it may well be an adaptation to bring the animal into the zone of the particular kind of plant plankton on which it feeds at different stages in its life-history. Behaviour of this kind is probably widespread among small aquatic forms and no doubt accounts, in part at least, for the characteristic positive phototaxis of *Hydra*, whose prey includes water-fleas and the larger Protozoa, which are to be found mainly in the well illuminated surface waters.

The penetration of light in static fresh water thus produces a situation comparable with that in the sea (see p. 118) where a vertical zonation of the plankton occurs. Temperature may also play some part in this process, but its effect is probably of secondary importance. Nightfall brings about a general upward movement of the animal species, each striving to attain its optimum illumination. The reverse takes place at dawn.

The depth to which light can penetrate varies greatly in different waters and is governed largely by the turbidity. A rough estimate for static regions is about 25 feet. Above this level a more or less abundant animal and plant community exists while below it the number of species rapidly decreases with the diminishing oxygen and food supply.

OXYGEN

Surface and shallow waters are generally saturated with oxygen in solution. The concentration varies from 5 to 10 c.c. per litre, and is dependent on temperature and pressure; that is to say, it is about one thirtieth of that in an equal volume of air. For whole-time aquatic organisms, it is thus vital that there should be a continuous renewal of the water in contact with the breathing surfaces if the requisite oxygen supply is to be maintained. A great variety of adaptations exist for this purpose, depending on the kind of habitat in which the animals live.

BREATHING IN SWIFTLY FLOWING WATER

The term 'swiftly flowing' will be used here to apply to regions of water with a minimum surface speed of 1 foot per second. This includes most shallow rivers and hill-side brooks, in which the rate of flow varies with the weather and time of year. (See Plate 14, at p. 161, and Fig. 31.)

In such habitats the water is permanently saturated with oxygen, and is thus able to support a fauna, much of which would be unable to survive in regions with poorer oxygenation.

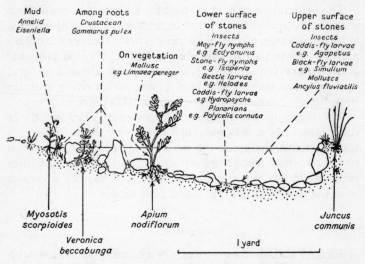

Fig. 31.—Profile chart across part of the stream in Plate 14 (at p. 161), showing some characteristic plants and animals.

Incidentally, another factor of great importance under these conditions is the strength of the current; for only those animals which are strong swimmers or possess some suitable means of anchorage will be able to avoid being washed away. This precludes colonization by surface-living forms possessing breathing tubes or unprotected spiracles, such as the larvae and pupae of gnats and midges, also aquatic Hemiptera like the Pond Skater (*Gerris*).

Many of the true colonists of swiftly flowing water absorb much, and sometimes all of their oxygen through the skin without adopting any special breathing organs. This is true of most young insect nymphs, for instance those of the stone-flies. Others, although possessing gills, are apparently capable of existing temporarily without them. Thus if the caudal gills of a young nymph of the Damsel Fly (*Agrion puella*) are removed,

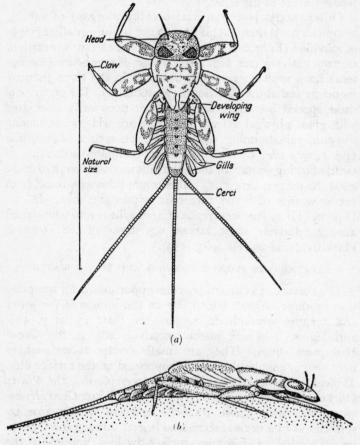

Fig. 32.—(*a*) Nymph of the common May-fly *Ecdyonurus venosus*. Note the well-developed abdominal gills.
(*b*) The nymph flattened when clinging to the surface of a stone.

(*After Mellanby*)

the animal continues its normal existence while new ones are being grown, although this is almost certainly accompanied by a slight reduction in viability. Many adults like planarians and leeches also habitually obtain their oxygen over the whole surface of the body.[1]

Other species possess special breathing organs of varying complexity. Abdominal gills are found in the aquatic nymphs of may-flies (Ephemeroptera), all of which can swim, crawl, or burrow actively (see Fig. 32). Those of stone-flies (Plecoptera) have similar structures, but only in the three thoracic segments and at the posterior of the abdomen. The presence of these special breathing organs is not necessarily associated with great physical activity, for they are widespread among sluggish, tube-building caddis-fly larvae such as *Limnophilus* and *Hydropsyche*, both of which are common occupants of swiftly flowing water. In these the gills no doubt serve to make good the oxygen deficiency which might otherwise result from the slow rate of water turn-over within the tube. In the Diptera (Flies) the occurrence of anal gills is also widespread among relatively static larvae, e.g. those of the common Black-fly, *Simulium* (Fig. 40 p. 159).

BREATHING IN SLOWLY FLOWING AND STATIC WATER

The absence of a current provides opportunities for colonization by those animals which live on the surface of the water and breathe atmospheric oxygen (see Plate 15, at p. 176, and Fig. 33). These insects mostly belong to the Order Hemiptera (Bugs). They are small, slender animals whose light weight enables them to be supported on the surface film. Typical examples are the Pond Skaters (*Gerris*), the Water Cricket (*Velia currens*), (see Fig. 34) and the Water Gnat (*Hydrometra stagnorum*), whose tracheae open to the exterior by spiracles as in a normal terrestrial insect. Among the Coleoptera (Beetles), a common surface-dwelling species is the Whirligig Beetle (*Gyrinus natator*).

Below the surface, to a distance which varies greatly in

---

[1] The larger the animal and, therefore, the smaller its surface-volume ratio, the less efficient does this method of respiration become.

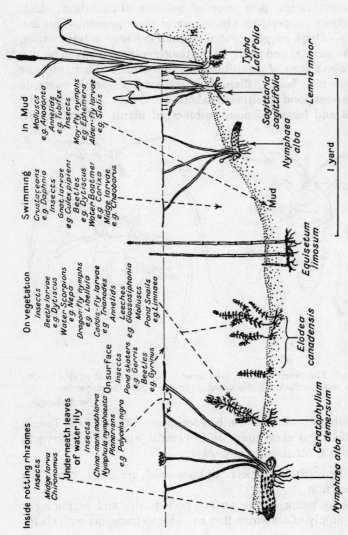

Inside rotting rhizomes
Insects
Midge larva
Chironomus

Underneath leaves
of water lily
Insects
China-mark mothlarva
Nymphula nymphaeata
Planarians
e.g. Polycelis nigra

On surface
Insects
Pond skaters
e.g. Gerris
Beetles
e.g. Gyrinus

On vegetation
Insects
Beetle larvae
e.g. Dytiscus
Water-Scorpions
e.g. Nepa
Dragon-Fly nymphs
e.g. Libellula
Caddis-Fly larvae
e.g. Trianodes
Annelids
Leeches
e.g. Glossosiphonia
Molluscs
Pond Snails
e.g. Limnaea

Swimming
Crustaceans
e.g. Daphnia
Insects
Gnat larvae
e.g. Culex pipiens
Beetles
e.g. Dytiscus
Water-Boatmer
e.g. Corixa
Midge larvae
e.g. Chaoborus

In Mud
Molluscs
e.g. Anodonta
Annelids
e.g. Tubifex
Insects
May-Fly nymphs
e.g. Ephemera
Alder-Fly larvae
e.g. Sialis

Typha Latifolia

Lemna minor

Sagittaria sagittifolia

Nymphaea alba

1 yard

Mud

Equisetum limosum

Elodea canadensis

Ceratophyllum demersum

Nymphaea alba

Fig. 33.—Profile chart across part of the canal in Plate 15 (at p. 176) to show some characteristic plants and animals.

different waters, is a zone of brilliant illumination which frequently supports an abundance of plant growth. This is a region of high oxygen concentration due partly to wave action on the surface, and partly to the photosynthesis of green plants. It is also a zone of plentiful food and therefore able to support an extensive fauna. Planarians and leeches (mostly parasitic on various pond snails) often abound and may be found on the stems and leaves of many submerged plants. These absorb

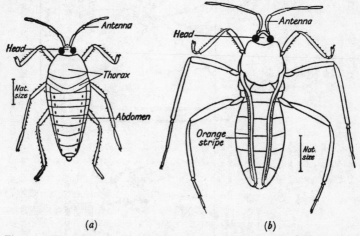

(a)   (b)

Fig. 34.—The Water Cricket (*Velia currens*). (a) Nymph; (b) adult. A common pond-skater inhabiting static and slowly flowing water.

(*After Mellanby*)

their oxygen all over the body-surface. Many of the insects found in this zone continue to breathe atmospheric oxygen, and this is obtained in two ways:

(i) By breathing tubes or siphons which are able to pierce the surface film.

(ii) By rising to the surface periodically and acquiring a fresh supply of air which they are able to transport with them.

In the first category are the aquatic larvae and pupae of Diptera such as the gnat *Culex pipiens*, also many Hemiptera like the Water Stick-insect (*Ranatra linearis*), the Water Scorpion (*Nepa cinerea*) and the larvae of many beetles such as *Dytiscus*. All these possess abdominal breathing siphons which they are able to project through the surface, either by attaching themselves to vegetation or by anchoring in the mud head downwards in shallow water (see Plate 16, at p. 177). This type of breathing mechanism has been carried to an extreme among the hover-flies (Syrphidae) notably *Eristalis tenax*, in which the so-called 'rat-tailed maggot' is provided with a long telescopic 'tail' which serves as a breathing tube, and may reach a length of 6 inches in the fully grown larva, itself only about 1 inch long (see Fig. 35).

In the second group are such actively swimming Hemiptera as the Water Boatman ('Back Swimmer') (*Notonecta*) and the Lesser Water Boatman (*Corixa*). These rise to the surface periodically to collect a fresh air-supply, which becomes entrapped as small bubbles in the space between the body and wings, also among the many hairs lining various parts of the body-surface. This gives the animal a silvery appearance which gradually diminishes as the air is absorbed through the spiracles in the thorax. A similar adaptation is found among aquatic beetles such as Great Diving Beetle (*Dytiscus marginalis*), in which air-pockets are enclosed by the elytra, also among the hairs lining the dorsal part of the abdomen. The Whirligig Beetle (*Gyrinus natator*), although strictly speaking a surface dweller, is also able to dive and swim actively when alarmed. On such occasions, a bubble of air can clearly be seen attached to the hind part of the abdomen entrapped among the fringing hairs. The numerous pond snails also come periodically to the surface for air, the mantle acting as a lung.

Most of the occupants of the well illuminated zone are true aquatic forms which derive the whole of their oxygen supply from the water. Many of the smaller insect larvae and nymphs absorb air through the whole of the body-surface, and these are without specialized breathing mechanisms. Others, like the nymphs of dragon-flies, have well-developed gills.

Most ponds and other areas of static water have a muddy

bottom where permanent residents are few, on account of a lack of food and sometimes a shortage of oxygen as well. Bivalve molluscs such as the Swan Mussel (*Anodonta cygnea*) which breathe by gills are often found here, provided the water is sufficiently aerated.

Among vertebrates, fishes are the most characteristic inhabitants of shallow water. Such species as the Loach

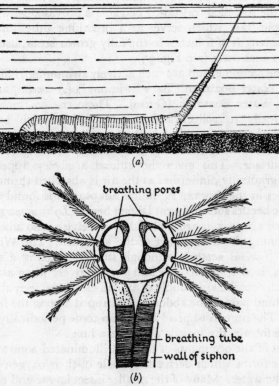

Fig. 35.—(*a*) The Rat-tailed Maggot of the Drone-fly (*Eristalis*). Note the breathing siphon suspended from the surface film (slightly enlarged). (*b*) Apex of the breathing siphon of the Rat-tailed Maggot. The fringe of hairs prevents water from entering the breathing pores. (Magnified.)

(*After Imms*)

(*Cobitis*) can absorb considerable quantities of oxygen through the wall of the intestine, and may be observed in an aquarium to rise periodically to the surface and swallow a mouthful of air. This enables it to make use of all parts of its habitat irrespective of oxygen supply, and also to withstand the drying up during the summer of the shallow ponds where it frequently lives.

OXYGEN SUPPLY IN DEEPER WATER

In deep lakes the conditions for life below the illuminated zone rapidly deteriorate. Oxygen replenishment is slow, while food is restricted to particles of detritus falling from the waters above. The chief colonists of this region are the larvae of various species of the midge *Chironomus*, all of which have a respiratory pigment similar to haemoglobin which accounts for their red colour. They are also to be found on the bottom of shallower waters, either burrowing in the mud or among rotting plant material such as the dead rhizomes of water lilies. Another common mud-dweller in deep water is the small tube-building annelid *Tubifex* which also possesses a respiratory pigment. When burrowing, the tail of the worm projects from its tube and acts as a gill. Other species include the ubiquitous nematode worms, also a few bivalve molluscs such as the Pea-shell Cockle (*Pisidium*).

INFLUENCE OF POLLUTION ON OXYGEN SUPPLY

Much organic material is constantly being added to fresh water as animals and plants die. Where there is a current this is rapidly washed away, but in slowly-moving and static waters, the action of bacteria and saprophytic fungi results in the breakdown of such debris into simpler substances which are ultimately returned to the water in the form of important manurial salts. The cycle of water purification and enrichment can only go on as long as conditions remain favourable. The addition of sewage and other undesirable substances by man, necessarily imposes a great strain on such a mechanism, and one of the first results is an exhaustion of the available oxygen. This causes the activities of aerobic micro-organisms to cease. Anaerobic bacteria are, however, capable of carrying on the process of decay, but these produce many poisonous and foul-smelling by-products such as hydrogen sulphide and numerous organic compounds. Thus pollution by man may quickly convert a stretch of water from a fertile plant and animal habitat into a region almost totally devoid of life, such as is found to-day in stretches of the Thames near London and in many other rivers running through the great industrial cities.

WATER: INFLUENCE OF DISSOLVED SALTS

Many of the substances dissolved in fresh water are essential for the life of its inhabitants. Floating plants are entirely dependent on the water for their mineral supplies since they have no connection with the mud below. These include such salts as nitrates, sulphates, and phosphates, which form the basis of plant proteins and are found in combination with a great variety of metals, the most important being calcium, potassium, magnesium, and iron. The presence of carbon dioxide is also essential for photosynthesis, and this normally occurs either in solution as carbonic acid, or in the form of bicarbonate.

In most fresh waters the concentration of minerals is low, seldom rising to more than a few parts per million. This is maintained by a cycle of events somewhat similar to that occurring in sea water (see p. 124). In spring the warmer weather results in a great outburst of plant activity which soon depletes available mineral supplies. In the absence of human influence, replacement is effected by the rotting of dead plants and animals which takes place to a small extent throughout the summer, but mainly during the autumn with the onset of lower temperatures. An important relationship thus exists between temperature and the supplies of oxygen, carbon dioxide, and salts (see Fig. 36). Another vital substance is silica, for this forms the outer covering of many diatoms which are characteristic members of the freshwater plankton. It is found that a marked reduction in the silica concentration occurs during the autumn, corresponding with the maximum development of diatoms, and a similar increase takes place in late spring when the small Crustacea are reaching their maximum density. The animals are unable to eat the shells of these minute plants, and as they are rejected they become available to increase the silicon supply once more.

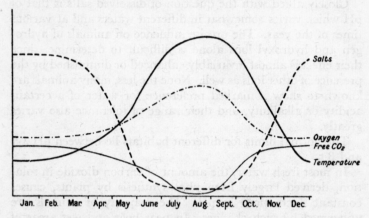

Fig. 36.—Diagram to show the approximate relationship existing between temperature, oxygen, free carbon dioxide, and mineral salts in shallow, static waters at different times of the year.

The presence of calcium salts also influences the distribution of some animals. For instance, crustaceans like the Freshwater Crayfish (*Astacus fluviatilis*) are never found in soft waters, since calcium compounds are essential for the formation of their exoskeleton. Many planarians have similar preferences, although the reason for them is not clear. It may be that these salts exert an effect on the permeability of the body tissues in a manner analogous to that found in some marine species such as *Procerodes ulvae* (see p. 113). Molluscs also have varying requirements for calcium. Thus the gastropod *Limnaea* is a typical inhabitant of hard waters, while the lamellibranch *Pisidium* only colonizes lime-free localities.

Trace substances probably also play an important part in fresh water just as they do in the sea. Our knowledge of them at present is, however, fragmentary, chiefly on account of the minute quantities in which they are found.

INFLUENCE OF HYDROGEN-ION CONCENTRATION

Closely allied with the question of dissolved salts is that of pH which varies somewhat in different waters and at various times of the year. The precise influence on animals of hydrogen and hydroxyl ions alone is difficult to determine, since their effect is almost invariably enhanced or diminished by the presence of other ions as well. None the less, many animals are known to show a marked preference for water of a certain acidity or alkalinity, and their range of tolerance also varies greatly.

The normal limits for different habitats lie between pH 4·7 and 8·5.

In most fresh water, the amount of carbon dioxide in solution, derived largely from photosynthesis by plants, causes constant fluctuations in pH. The majority of animals are unharmed by such changes. In peat bogs and wet areas of moorland, anaerobic decomposition of dead plant matter produces acid conditions with a pH often less than 4·7. Most species are unable to live in these regions, some exceptions being the larvae of mosquitoes such as *Finlaya geniculata* and *Anopheles plumbeus* which habitually breed in pools found in the holes of rotting tree-stumps. These develop only in an extremely acid environment (about pH 4·4). In moorland streams there is generally a total absence of life at the source, where the pH may be as low as 4·5. Numerous species are capable of colonizing the less acid regions (about pH 5·5) such as the Freshwater Shrimp (*Gammarus pulex*), the River Limpet (*Ancylus fluviatilis*), also many planarians and larvae of caddis-flies.

Most animals are found experimentally to have a tolerance of pH far beyond anything which they normally experience. For instance the nymph of the dragon-fly *Libellula pulchella*, commonly inhabits ponds and other areas of shallow, static water with pH 7–8. In the laboratory it has been shown to withstand successfully as high an acidity as pH 1.

In flowing water, fluctuations in hydrogen-ion concentration are never so extreme as in static areas. This is due to the constant movement which tends to even out the various chemical changes taking place in the different regions.

CURRENT

In streams and rivers, small animals constantly face the danger of being washed away. Various methods have been evolved to overcome this, the general tendency being to reduce the area of the body exposed to the current. A typical example among fishes is the Bullhead (*Cottus gobio*), in which the head is much compressed dorso-ventrally, enabling it to lurk on the bottom facing the current in the shelter of stones or vegetation without the necessity for active swimming. Many aquatic insects such as may-fly nymphs are also flattened (see Fig. 32), and when clinging to stones, offer the minimum of resistance to the water. The larvae of most caddis-flies are able to anchor themselves to the substratum while remaining within a case or web. This is made of a variety of materials such as sand grains, small stones, or pieces of vegetation and is often beautifully streamlined, as in *Leptocerus* and *Limnophilus*. In some species such as *Agapetus*, the anchorage of the larval cases is so efficient that they are able to withstand the full force of the current in mid-stream, and these frequently encrust the upper surface of stones.

Many stream and river animals tend to face or move upstream against the current (positive rheotaxis). No doubt the physical impact of the current on the animal's body, and the visual stimulus of the passage of particles in the water are two of the most important factors concerned. Such behaviour serves to keep the animal within the locality best suited to its requirements, and to ensure a copious supply of food. Some planarians when kept experimentally in static water, appear to undergo a physiological change and lose the power of positive rheotaxis altogether. In certain circumstances, for instance a change of temperature, their response to the current may actually be reversed. Similarly, the Ice Age relict *Planaria alpina* is positively rheotactic (swims up-stream) when its reproductive organs are developing, but becomes negatively rheotactic after its eggs have been laid.

Responses to the current are sometimes closely associated with those to light. For example, the nymphs of many mayflies such as *Ecdyonurus* shun bright light, and invariably seek the shady under-sides of stones where, moreover, they are unlikely to be washed away. It has been shown that the current itself also plays a part in this response, for if the animals are transferred to static water their reaction to light almost ceases after about one hour, but can be restored when the nymphs are returned to stream conditions once more. This kind of situation where two or more distinct factors interact to govern a single response is probably widespread among lower forms. Weak swimmers like the Freshwater Shrimp (*Gammarus pulex*) frequently find protection behind stones or among the roots of aquatic plants; while active species are able to burrow into the sand or mud of the stream-bed, notably the nymphs of such may-flies as *Ephemera*. Many caddis-fly larvae are able to provide their own anchorage, and are therefore to some extent independent of natural shelter.

INFLUENCE OF BIOTIC FACTORS. FOOD

As in the sea, so in fresh water, the fauna can be divided roughly into herbivores, carnivores, and detritus feeders. The community of smaller plants forms a vital link in all their food chains, and in this respect static and swiftly flowing waters differ somewhat.

In streams and rivers most of the plant plankton is removed by the current, also any animals like small crustaceans which feed on it. This seriously reduces the amount of food available for the resident carnivores, and largely accounts for the small number of species found in swiftly flowing water as compared with those of static and slowly flowing regions.

Herbivores. Surprisingly few freshwater animals feed on the larger plants. Where there is an abundant plant plankton, this supports an extensive community of minute animals, mainly Protozoa and Crustacea, such as the water-fleas (Cladocera) and many copepods. These are an important source of food for the aquatic carnivores (see Fig. 37).

Among vertebrates, all amphibian larvae are herbivores for the greater part of their life, feeding on a variety of small aquatic plants. Invertebrate herbivores include the gastropod molluscs, notably the River Limpet (*Ancylus*) which inhabits flowing water, the Pond Snails (*Limnaea*) and Trumpet Snails (*Planorbis*) which are common inhabitants of ponds and shallow lakes. All these feed on various minute green algae, and are thus a useful means of removing algal slime from the sides of aquaria and ornamental pools. An unusual group of static water herbivores are the larvae of the China-mark Moths (Pyralidae), one of the commonest being the Brown China-mark (*Nymphula nymphaeata*). Its food plant is the Water Lily, and during early life the larva can often be identified by the peculiar shelter which it constructs, consisting of an oval piece of leaf attached to another on the under-side. At this stage the spiracles are closed and breathing takes place entirely through the skin. Another moth of unusual habits is *Acentropus niveus* (Pyraustidae) whose larva feeds on a number of aquatic plants, especially *Ceratophyllum*, and pupates deep in the water. The adult male is always winged, while the female occurs in two phases, one with wings (which it uses for active flying), the other almost wingless which remains submerged.

Numerous beetles are also true herbivores either as larvae, adults, or both, a common example being *Haliplus* which is closely allied to the Great Diving Beetle (*Dytiscus*). This is common in many ponds, the larva feeding on filamentous green algae such as *Spirogyra*.

Carnivores. Nearly all the larger freshwater animals are carnivorous. These include such surface-dwelling insects as

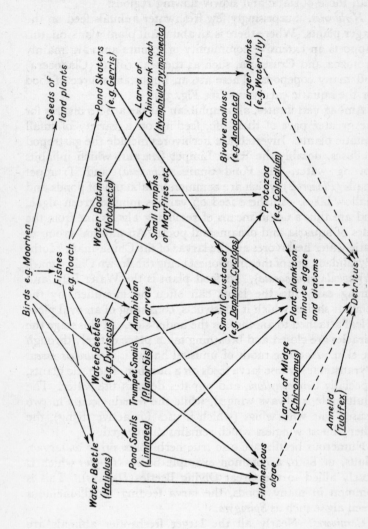

Fig. 37.—Some food chains of animals inhabiting static, fresh water.

the Water Gnat (*Hydrometra*), the Pond Skater (*Gerris*) and the Water Cricket (*Velia*), all of which feed either on small insects occupying the surface film, or on the minute crustaceans immediately below it (see Fig. 38).

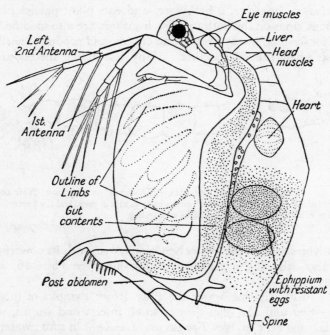

Fig. 38.—The small crustacean *Daphnia*, side view (actual length 2 mm.). A characteristic member of the animal plankton in static, fresh water.

(*After Mellanby*)

The larger swimming forms are also mostly carnivores and many of them possess special feeding structures. The Great Diving Beetle (*Dytiscus marginalis*) devours tadpoles, small molluscs, and many other insects while its larva is equally predaceous, possessing powerful hooked mandibles. Many other aquatic beetles have the same habits. Among

Hemiptera, the Water Boatman (*Notonecta*) feeds on small minnows, tadpoles, and even members of its own species. The forelegs are well developed for seizing prey, while the third pair have become greatly expanded to provide powerful swimming organs. Its near relative the Lesser Water Boatman (*Corixa*) is, however, a herbivore, and eats plant particles of various kinds on the bottom. The front legs are also modified, not for feeding, but as stridulating organs, and produce a shrill noise when rubbed together. Many less active species are

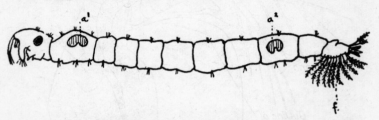

Fig. 39.—Larva of the Phantom Midge, *Chaoborus*. ×7 approx. Note the internal air sacs (a^1 and a^2) which act as hydrostatic organs, and the posterior tuft of filamentous hairs (f) used in swimming.

(*After Carpenter*)

carnivores such as the Water Scorpion (*Nepa*) with its powerful forelegs, also the nymphs of dragon-flies (see Plate 16, at p. 177).

In swiftly flowing water the fully grown nymphs of most stone-flies and may-flies devour small insects and worms, so do larvae of the midges *Tanypus* and *Chaoborus* in static waters (see Fig. 39).

Detritus Feeders. The rotting remains of dead plants and animals constantly provide large quantities of detritus in various stages of decomposition. These gradually accumulate on the bottom, particularly in areas where the current is insufficient to wash them away. Static waters are thus particularly favourable for colonization by detritus-feeding animals, most of which are crawling or burrowing forms.

The largest of these are the bivalve molluscs, notably the Swan Mussel (*Anodonta cygnea*) and the Freshwater Mussel

(*Unio pictorum*), both of which are ciliary feeders, and capable of ploughing their way through the mud by means of a muscular 'foot' at a rate of approximately a mile a year.

The smaller animals include the larva of the midge

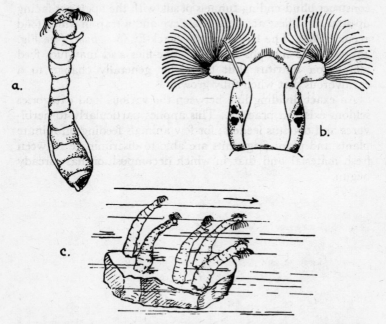

Fig. 40.—Larvae of the Black-fly (*Simulium*). (*a*) A single larva viewed from the side. × 2½ approx. (*b*) Dorsal view of head (much enlarged) to show current-producing organs, antennae, and eye spots (*after Miall*). (*c*) A group of larvae attached to a stone in flowing water. (Natural size.)

(*After Carpenter*)

Chironomus, which filters organic particles from mud stirred up by wriggling its body. The small annelid *Tubifex*, feeds by engulfing mud like an earthworm, any nutrient material being extracted during its passage through the gut.

The wheel animalcules (Rotifera) are ciliary feeders, and occur in both static and flowing waters, their diet being a mixture of detritus and fresh plant plankton. In swiftly flowing waters, a few species are well adapted for collecting particles washed down-stream. The case-building larvae of the caddis-flies *Trianodes*, *Stenophylax*, and *Agapetus*, are typical examples. Some, such as *Hydropsyche* are web-spinners and construct blind-ending tunnels of silk with the openings facing up-stream. These act both as a sieve and a trap in which food accumulates. The larvae of the Black-fly (*Simulium*) (see Fig. 40), also the nymphs of most stone-flies and may-flies feed mainly on detritus, but the latter generally change to a carnivorous diet when fully grown.

An exact dividing line between the various food categories seldom exists in practice. This applies particularly to herbivores and detritus feeders; for few animals feeding on minute plants and plant fragments are able to discriminate between fresh material and that in which decomposition has already begun.

13. CONDITIONS IN AN ESTUARY (RIVER EXE). NOTE THE DENSE GROWTH OF RUSHES (*Juncus maritimus*) STANDING IN POOLS OF BRACKISH WATER AND THE MUD FLATS, EXPOSED AT LOW TIDE

14. A SHALLOW AND SWIFTLY FLOWING STREAM (*Eppscleave Wood, Near Tiverton*)
(See also Fig. 31, p. 142)

CHAPTER IX

PRACTICAL ANIMAL ECOLOGY

In the following pages an attempt has been made to describe in a concise form some of the apparatus and simple techniques which will be found useful in the elementary study of ecology. The subject is now a vast one, and for a more detailed treatment, the reader is referred to my *Practical Animal Ecology* (Methuen) in which modern methods are described, also the circumstances in which they can be applied.

APPARATUS

One advantage of ecological studies is the relatively inexpensive apparatus they require. Apart from the standard equipment of any biology laboratory such as microscopes, much of the additional material can be home-made. In the following pages emphasis is laid on the use of accessories which can be constructed in the laboratory, and reference to expensive items has been avoided wherever possible.

Any standard microscope with high- and low-power objectives will generally be suitable for the identification of smaller animals and plants. In addition, a low-power binocular dissecting microscope will be found useful for examining material such as the larger insect larvae and nymphs, particularly when these are alive. A good hand-lens is also indispensable, and students should be encouraged to overcome their usual reluctance to use one. A magnification of ×8 will be found convenient for most purposes.

COLLECTING EQUIPMENT

In any ecological work requiring collecting, the first requirement is a good supply of containers. These may be of many kinds depending on the nature of the habitat to be studied. In general, glass specimen tubes with well-fitting corks will be suitable for all except the larger animals, while small pill-boxes serve well for most terrestrial insects.

Before setting out, all containers should bear a blank label on the body of the container itself, *NOT* on the cork or lid (as these may be interchangeable), on which can be recorded the locality and other data *directly the specimens are obtained*. The small amount of trouble involved in this preliminary measure will prove to be well worth while in avoiding muddle and inaccuracy when the results are eventually sorted out.

(*a*) *Collecting on Land*. By far the commonest terrestrial animals collected in ecological work are insects. No reference will be made here to the kind of traps suitable for obtaining the larger animals.

For catching actively flying species such as butterflies, moths, flies, etc., a suitable net is required with a short stick not more than about 2 feet long. Entomological nets are best obtained from a dealer. They are of a more or less standard pattern with a diameter of about 18 inches, and a jointed frame to permit folding. The net bag is made of leno and this should be black so that the insects inside it can be more easily seen. The so-called Kite Net will be found the best shape and size for most insect collecting.

Larvae feeding on bushes and trees are conveniently collected by beating the vegetation with a stick and catching the insects as they fall off. For this purpose a 'tray' is required, consisting of a piece of strong fabric about 1 yard square, kept taut by a wooden frame. This should be collapsible in order to facilitate transport. The standard pattern Bignell Beating Tray can be purchased but this is rather expensive, and a suitable substitute can easily be made in the laboratory. I have used an old umbrella for many years with considerable success.

When collecting insects in the field it is often necessary to kill them for ease of transport. This is best done in a bottle filled with a mixture of potassium cyanide and plaster of Paris to a depth of about an inch. The bottle should have a wide neck and well-fitting cork (not a screw top), and can easily be obtained from a dealer. It will be found that corks are all too often cut with the lenticels running along their length instead of transversely. These are not gas-tight, and if used as they are, the killing bottle will deteriorate rapidly. The difficulty can be overcome by dipping the cork in molten paraffin wax which will block the pores and keep the bottle effective for several years. The cyanide bottle has an advantage over other kinds in being easily made-up (any chemist's shop will do this), lasting well, and damaging but few insect pigments. Remember that the gas is *poisonous*. In order to prevent the specimens from rubbing against the rough surface at the bottom of the bottle, it is advisable to cover it with a thin layer of cotton-wool.

For collecting very small insects, such as beetles on the bark of trees, an empty wash-bottle with a nozzle of suitable aperture will be found helpful. The specimens can then be sucked into the flask without difficulty.

(b) *Collecting in Water*. Many of the larger aquatic animals can be collected by hand. For this purpose a strong penknife will be found useful, not only in prising species such as limpets and sea anemones off rocks, but also in transferring the smallest forms such as the larvae and nymphs of insects into specimen tubes.

For collecting the larger animals in such localities as ponds, streams, and rock pools, some kind of water net is necessary. This should have a stout metal frame which may be any shape ranging from square to circular, depending on the kind of habitat. A convenient diameter is about 8 inches, and the bag should be made of a strong material which is not easily torn. The length of the stick must also vary with circumstances, but it is seldom necessary to exceed 6 feet. Transport is often a primary consideration, and in this respect a sectional wooden rod of convenient lengths which can be unscrewed, is a great help. This can be obtained quite cheaply. In flowing water such as small streams, animals inhabiting the surface of stones or vegetation are easily dislodged and lost. This difficulty can often be overcome by arranging the net a short distance downstream from the collecting point, and placing stones so that the animals cannot pass by on either side.

The minute animals and plants (plankton) inhabiting static

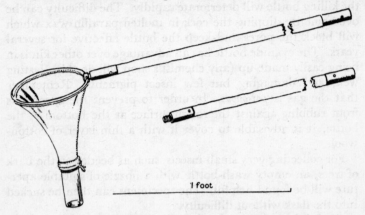

1 foot

Fig. 41.—Plankton net fitted with a sectional rod.

water are collected in a Plankton Net (see Fig. 41). This consists of a fine mesh net narrowing funnel-wise to the mouth of a glass tube into which the organisms are swept. The other end is fastened to a frame which may be square or circular, the most usual diameter being about 5 inches. For collecting from a bank or rocks a stick attachment is necessary, its length being determined by much the same considerations as for the water net. Plankton nets for towing behind a boat are fitted with ropes. These are often of large size and usually have a diameter of 11 inches or more.

Animals living in the sand or mud of ponds, rivers, and shallow offshore waters are most conveniently collected by means of a Drag-net (see Fig. 42). This has a thick rectangular metal frame generally about 12 ×6 inches, fitted with a strong bag approximately 18 inches deep. The net is pulled along by cords attached to the sides of the frame. Larger models can, of course, be used when towed behind a boat, but these tend to be heavy and cumbersome to carry.

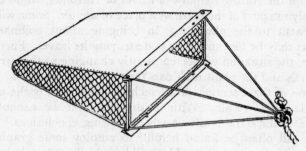

Fig. 42.—Drag-net with rope attachment.

TYPES OF PROBLEM AND TREATMENT OF RESULTS

There are many lines of approach to every ecological problem as we have already seen in Chapter I. In practice, it is seldom possible or desirable to follow more than a few of these at a time.

Most studies inevitably demand consideration of one or more of the following aspects:

(a) Distribution.
(b) Ecological factors.
(c) Quantitative problems.

For the purpose of convenience these will be discussed separately, although in fact they are always closely interrelated.

DISTRIBUTION

Studies of animal distribution are most easily conducted in some well defined habitat such as a wood, stream, or rock pool. The animals are collected or observed, identified, and their location recorded relative to their surroundings. Interesting results can often be obtained from an examination of the fauna associated with a particular species of plant at various times of the year. Some forms will feed on it, and it may be possible to show that these have their own parasites and predators—in this way the idea of food chains can be built up. Others may feed on the rotting remains of leaves or rhizomes, while some merely use part of the plant as a place of shelter. Some will be a benefit to the plant, e.g. in bringing about pollination, others may be harmful in, say, destroying its leaves. Furthermore, the situation will be constantly changing as the various animals and the plant itself pass through their life-cycles.

One of the essentials of all such investigations is the clear tabulation of results. Without this, the best use cannot be made of the data available when drawing conclusions.

It will often be found helpful to employ some graphical means of representation. This will be subsidiary to tabulation and should never be employed alone. The *profile chart* is a useful method of showing the relationship of plants and animals in, say, a pond or on the seashore (see Figs. 25, 31 and 33). It is intended to give a picture from a vertical standpoint. By contrast, the *transect* provides a plan from a horizontal point of view. Both of these should be as simple as possible, and clearly drawn, avoiding all unnecessary lines and shading. Above all they must be *fully labelled*. Elaborate maps are seldom necessary in practical animal ecology, and an excessive amount of time can be wasted in constructing them.

INFLUENCE OF CLIMATIC FACTORS

We have seen in the previous Chapters how fluctuations in the physical environment may bring about great changes in the behaviour and distribution of animals. For instance, the influence of sudden variations in temperature during spring and autumn on the occupants of a small pond is often quite remarkable. A rise of only a few degrees accompanied by sunshine causes a great increase in plant photosynthesis, and the water may soon be swarming with small algae and diatoms. These use up the carbon dioxide and liberate oxygen thereby causing a marked change in pH. At the same time the small animals such as crustaceans and insect larvae may become active, and can be seen under a microscope to feed eagerly on the minute plants. Observations of this kind can be fascinating and, if organized properly, need not consume a disproportionate amount of time.

Little need be said about the recording and analysis of climatic variations; some methods of measurement will be described shortly in the next section. Clearly a suitable system of tabulation is required, and the results are best shown graphically. If possible, related readings should be plotted on the same sheet, one above the other, as this greatly facilitates comparison.

MEASUREMENT OF CLIMATIC FACTORS

Temperature. The mercury thermometer has many uses in ecology both for measuring temperature, and also for recording humidity by the wet- and dry-bulb method. In static water it is often necessary to find the temperature gradient below the surface by taking readings at various levels, and plotting these against depth on a graph. For this purpose an ordinary maximum and minimum thermometer can be used attached to a line[1] with knots tied in it at known distances apart. The method has two disadvantages if any degree of precision is required. In the first place, this kind of thermometer tends to be rather insensitive and inaccurate, furthermore, it cannot be used as a continuously recording instrument without removal from the water, and resetting after each reading.

An ingenious device known as a 'Thermistor' has recently been developed by Standard Telephones and Cables Ltd., and costs only a few shillings. This consists of a small capsule containing a complex metal oxide compound whose resistance decreases rapidly with increasing temperature. Used in a simple Wheatstone Bridge circuit it acts as a sensitive thermometer, and has the great advantage of being continuously recording (see Fig. 43). For each measurement, the variable resistance R_3 is adjusted until no reading is obtained on the galvanometer. When finding the temperature of water, the 'Thermistor' (T) can be attached to a calibrated rod and

[1] This should be made of plastic (e.g. nylon) which does not shrink when wet.

low-resistance leads fitted to it. It is important that these, also all joints, should be well insulated with waterproof material. The variable resistance (R3) is provided by a rheostat fitted with a degree scale, while a small torch battery (B) and relatively inexpensive moving-coil galvanometer (G) are the only additional items required.[1] Before use, a simple conversion graph must be constructed in the laboratory by immersing the

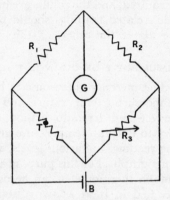

Fig. 43.—Wheatstone Bridge circuit for use with a 'Thermistor'.

'Thermistor' in water of varying temperatures (measured by a sensitive mercury thermometer) and plotting these against the corresponding values of R3. When doing this it is important to use the same leads from the 'Thermistor' as will be used in the field.

Light Intensity. A quickly acting and sensitive light-meter can be quite easily home-made. One type commonly described makes use of Rhodamine B paper. This, however, requires considerable preparation, and has a number of other drawbacks.

By far the most satisfactory method of measuring illumina-

[1] The complete apparatus (known as a 'Logohm') can be obtained as a single compact unit which is easily transportable. Manufactured by the Baldwin Instrument Co. Ltd.

tion is by means of an instrument employing a photo-voltaic cell, calibrated in foot-candles. Various types are now available and, if necessary, a photographic exposure meter can be

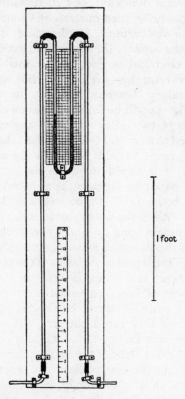

1 foot

Fig. 44.—Apparatus for measuring the rate of flow of a current.

adapted for the purpose. It should be remembered that such instruments are not waterproof. Moreover, before use they should be calibrated against a commercial light-meter in foot-candles.[1]

[1] For details of the construction and calibration of a waterproof photo-voltaic light-meter see, Dowdeswell, W. H. and Humby, S. R. (1953), *School Science Review*, **125**, 64.

Current. The simplest method of measuring the rate of flow of, say, a small stream is to put some light object in the water and record the time taken to travel a given distance. This procedure has the obvious disadvantage that it is affected by the wind, also it can only be used in straight stretches of water where there are no obstructions. Furthermore, it only measures the current at the surface; this decreases considerably with depth.

Various electrical devices can be used for measuring the speed of a current; these are accurate but not easily constructed in the laboratory. For most ordinary purposes the apparatus shown in Fig. 44 will be found satisfactory. It is easily made, and consists of two tubes with right-angled bends at one end and attached to a central U-tube at the other. This is partially filled with water, suitably coloured by some stain such as Orange G. The board to which the tubes are attached is calibrated, so that the depth of the right-angled tubes below the surface can be read off. A piece of graph paper is fixed behind the U-tube. When the apparatus is immersed in flowing water with the tubes pointing up- and down-stream, the differing air pressure on the two sides causes a corresponding difference in the height of the liquid in the arms of the U-tube. To calibrate the instrument, this value is read off and plotted against different rates of flow (estimated most conveniently at the surface of a suitable stream by the floating object method). For all except very rapid currents, the relationship will be found to be nearly linear, so that it is only necessary to multiply the difference in height of the liquid columns by a constant in order to obtain the rate of flow. In practice, the apparatus will be found to have one small defect, namely that air-locks readily occur at the right-angled bends of the two tubes. These can be quickly detected, for the columns of liquid in the U-tube will be at different heights. They can be removed easily by means of a pipe-cleaner or flexible plant stem;[1] it is important to ensure that the two sides are level before taking a reading. It is a wise precaution to construct at least the

[1] A sharp knock on the side of the board will generally have the desired effect.

lower part of the apparatus of metal tubing rather than glass, in order to avoid continual breakage.

Dissolved Oxygen. Oxygen in solution can be conveniently estimated by Winkler's method. The first requisite is a sample

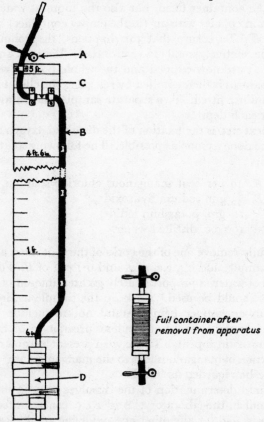

Fig. 45.—Apparatus for collecting a sample of water from a river, pond or shallow lake.

of water which has not been brought into contact with air during the course of collection. This can be obtained by means of the apparatus shown in Fig. 45. The empty container D is lowered to the required depth, as shown on the graduated stick. The clip at A is now released, and water sucked up until it fills the rubber tube B. In order to avoid a mouthful, a small piece of glass tubing C is inserted at right angles near A to give warning of the water level. Thus, not only is the container filled, but also the topmost water which has been in contact with air (in the empty container) has been drawn off. To ensure that this happens, the volume of D should be relatively small (100 c.c. or less). The inlet and outlet tubes of D are now clipped and the whole portion removed. The apparatus is then emptied by releasing the clip at A and a new container fitted. Two separate samples should always be taken at each depth.

The next step is the fixation of the dissolved oxygen and this should be done as soon as possible. The following solutions are required:

A. 40 per cent manganous chloride solution.
B. 33 gm. sodium hydroxide,
   10 gm. potassium iodide,
   100 c.c. distilled water.

Carefully remove one of the corks of the container, and for a 70 c.c. sample, add 0·5 c.c. of A and 0·1 c.c. of B. For larger volumes of water, a proportionately greater amount of the two solutions should be used. Cork up the sample again with a plain rubber stopper being careful not to include any air bubbles. Shake well. A flocculent precipitate of hydrated manganic oxide appears. The oxygen present has now oxidized a proportion of manganous ions to the manganic state, and can therefore be regarded as 'fixed'.

The final determination of the dissolved oxygen should be carried out in the laboratory. Add 2 c.c. concentrated ortho-phosphoric acid (or any other non-oxidizing acid). Restopper and shake until all the precipitate has dissolved. The manganic ions in the acid medium have now released an equivalent amount of iodine from the potassium iodide. Extract 25 c.c. in a pipette and titrate against N/80 sodium thiosulphate in the usual way, using freshly made starch solution as an indicator.

Do not add the starch until the yellow of the iodine has nearly disappeared, and continue titration until the resulting blue colour is just destroyed. This procedure should be repeated at least twice for each sample.

The calculation is then as follows:

1 c.c. N/80 sodium thiosulphate is equivalent to 0·1 mg. oxygen. Let V be the volume of thiosulphate used, and v the volume of the sample.

Then

$$\frac{V \times 0 \cdot 1 \times 100}{v} \text{ mg. oxygen per 100 c.c.}$$
$$= \text{parts oxygen per 100,000 by weight.}$$

To express the result in c.c. oxygen per litre at N.T.P. the following formula is used:

1 c.c. N/80 thiosulphate $\equiv$ 0·0001 gr. oxygen.

Hence 1 c.c. N/80 thiosulphate $\equiv \dfrac{0 \cdot 0001 \times 22400}{32}$ c.c. oxygen.

Hence

$$\frac{V \times 0 \cdot 0001 \times 22400 \times 1,000}{32 \times v} = \frac{V \times 70}{v}$$
$$= \text{c.c. oxygen per litre at N.T.P.}$$

This method is found to work well in practice, and the only likely cause of failure, apart from the accidental inclusion of oxygen in the water sample, is the slow oxidation of the potassium iodide in solution B with the liberation of appreciable quantities of iodine. For this reason a fresh supply should be made up whenever a yellow colour appears. It must also be remembered that solutions A and B will themselves contain appreciable quantities of oxygen. For comparative purposes this does not matter, provided the same amounts are added to each sample of water. For accurate estimation of oxygen content, minimum quantities of the two solutions must always be used. Should it be necessary to work with large volumes, the error involved can readily be determined by first using a sample of boiled distilled water.

The most convenient way of expressing the amount of dissolved oxygen is as a percentage of the saturation value for a particular temperature. This can be done by reference to Table 1 below.

Temp. (°C.)	mg. Oxygen per litre water	cc. Oxygen per litre at N.T.P.
5	12·3	8·68
6	12·05	8·49
7	11·80	8·31
8	11·55	8·13
9	11·29	7·95
10	11·03	7·77
11	10·79	7·60
12	10·56	7·44
13	10·34	7·28
14	10·11	7·12
15	9·88	6·96
16	9·68	6·82
17	9·48	6·68
18	9·28	6·54
19	9·08	6·40
20	8·92	6·28

TABLE 1. Oxygen dissolved by distilled water when saturated with air at different temperatures. (*After Roscoe and Lunt*)

Dissolved Carbon Dioxide. The amount of carbon dioxide in water will generally vary inversely with the dissolved oxygen when plants and animals are present. The most accurate means of estimation is by Trillick's Method. This, however, involves the use of baryta which is extremely difficult to handle successfully, and so will not be considered here.

The free carbon dioxide present in *acid* water can be estimated with sufficient accuracy for most practical purposes by observing the colour change in alkaline phenolphthalein solution when a known volume of the sample under test is added. Prepare a N/20 solution of sodium carbonate by dissolving 2·65 gm. of the pure solid in boiled distilled water. Add 2·5 gm. phenolphthalein and make up to 1 litre. Titrate 100 c.c. of water (collected in the same way as for the determination of dissolved oxygen) against this solution until a permanent pink colour is obtained. A zero point correction of 0·5 c.c. is deducted from the volume required, and the remainder multiplied by 1·22 (instead of the theoretical 1·1). This gives the mg. of free carbon dioxide in 100 c.c. of water. The method works reliably, and with a little practice it is quite easy to decide when the end-point in the titration has been reached. The water sample should be in as small a container as possible, fitted with a cork.

When water is *neutral* or *alkaline*, any carbon dioxide present will be in the form of bicarbonate. This can be estimated using 1 : 1,000 methyl orange as indicator. A few drops of indicator are added to 50 c.c. of the water sample in a container fitted with a cork. Titrate with N/25 hydrochloric acid, replacing the cork after each addition of acid to exclude any free carbon dioxide. The acid must be standardized against sodium hydroxide using phenolphthalein as indicator. 1 mg. of carbon dioxide as bicarbonate is equivalent to 0·83 mg. hydrochloric acid.

Salinity. A convenient method of determining the total chlorides present in a sample of sea or brackish water is by a silver nitrate titration. Prepare a 0·114 N solution by dissolving 19·37 gm. of oven-dry solid in a litre of distilled water. Place 10 c.c. of the water sample in a test-tube, and add 2 drops of 10 per cent potassium chromate solution. Run in the silver nitrate from a burette and shake periodically with the thumb over the end of the tube. The end-point is reached when a red colour appears. 1 c.c. of 0·114 N silver nitrate is equivalent to 2 per cent sea water in a 10 c.c. sample. Although subject to slight variation, the sea water around our coasts can be regarded for all practical purposes as containing 3·1 per cent chlorides.

It is important to remember that this method is only accurate for concentrations up to 20 per cent sea water. For higher salinities it is necessary to dilute the sample appropriately.

Hydrogen-Ion Concentration (pH). The pH of soil or water is readily determined with sufficient accuracy for most purposes by the use of a multiple indicator, such as the B.D.H. Soil Indicator. Water samples are collected as for dissolved oxygen estimation (see p. 171). A small volume is poured into a clean test-tube and a little indicator added. The resulting colour is matched against the chart provided and the corresponding pH noted.

Since soils are well buffered, they can be diluted considerably with distilled water without altering the pH. It is therefore unnecessary to use any particular weight. A small amount is placed in a test-tube, and an equal quantity of precipitated barium sulphate added. The tube is shaken well, and as the barium sulphate settles to the bottom, it carries with it most of the colloidal particles in suspension leaving a clear liquid above. The indicator is now added and the pH obtained as for a water sample. The British Drug Houses, Ltd., supply a compact case containing all the equipment required.[1] This is inexpensive and ideal for use in the field. Surprisingly little is known about the influence of the pH on animals inhabiting soil, and this might well prove a profitable line of enquiry. Its effect on plants has been studied in far greater detail, in fact, the composition of a flora can now be used as a gauge of the conditions in the soil below.

QUANTITATIVE PROBLEMS. SAMPLING

Ideally, the density of a population should be determined by counting every individual. Such a procedure obviously has its limitations, and can be used only with large animals such as birds, and in small colonies of species inhabiting isolated or restricted localities. In all other instances a method of sampling must be adopted.

In studying plants, the most usual means of sampling a population is by counting the individuals in a standard square (*quadrat*) laid down at random in a number of different places. In this way, information such as the relative abundance of

---

[1] For more accurate determinations, a B.D.H. capillator outfit will be found useful. This gives estimates to the nearest 0·2 pH. The price ranges between one and four pounds.

15. AN AREA OF STATIC WATER (GRAND WESTERN CANAL, TIVERTON) WITH PROLIFIC GROWTH OF REED MACE (*Typha latifolia*) AND WHITE WATER-LILY (*Nymphaea alba*)

(See also Fig. 33, p. 145)

(*a*)　Water Scorpion (*Nepa cinerea*). The long breathing
tube has penetrated the surface

(*b*)　Nymph of the Emperor Dragonfly (*Anax imperator*)
eating a worm. Note the use of the 'mask' in gripping
its prey

16.　TWO COMMON CARNIVOROUS INSECTS INHABITING
STATIC FRESH WATER

different species can be determined. It is also possible to estimate the density of the population as a whole.[1] The method can only be used for relatively static animals such as insect larvae. Further, they must be present in fair numbers if a large sampling error is to be avoided.

Random samples of an animal population are most easily obtained with small swimming or flying species. For instance, fluctuations in the plankton inhabiting static fresh water can be conveniently studied. Here sampling must be carried out with a net along a fixed line, at a constant depth, and over a prearranged distance. The density can be determined either by counting the number of individuals under the microscope in a small diluted sample (this is tedious and rather inaccurate), or as bulk dry-weight. The second method is more accurate and quicker, but assumes that the amount of colloidal matter suspended in the water is constant, since it is not possible to separate it readily from the organisms themselves. This generally constitutes such a small proportion of the total weight that the error involved is negligible. The organisms are best collected on a filter-paper (previously weighed) through a Büchner funnel[2] and dried on a steam bath. It is important to remember that samples of this kind, particularly if they are small and variable, may give little indication of the condition of the population from which they are withdrawn; thus due caution must be exercised in generalizing from them. The results are best presented in the form of a histogram, dry-weight being plotted on the Y and time along the X axis.

Similar sampling methods can be employed for flying insects, such as colonies of butterflies. Care should be taken to randomize collecting as much as possible by covering the whole area of the habitat equally, irrespective of the distribution of the animals at any particular moment.

STATISTICAL SIGNIFICANCE OF SAMPLES

We constantly need to describe populations of animals in

[1] For a comprehensive account of quantitative methods see, Greig-Smith, P. (1957), *Quantitative Plant Ecology*; Butterworth.

[2] A wide porcelain funnel used in conjunction with a filter-pump.

terms of some quality which we are studying. The appropriate way of doing so is to catch a *sample* of them and calculate its mean, which is merely a technical term indicating the measure which common sense would dictate; that is to say, its mathematical average. For instance, we may wish to study such variable characteristics as height, weight, or colour. The methods for doing this, and for relating the mean of the sample to that of the whole population from which it has been withdrawn may be obtained from any book on statistical methods[1] (see Bibliography).

However, *percentages* must frequently be calculated even in the most elementary stages of an ecological enquiry. Here again, we wish to know the extent to which a sample reflects the conditions in the community as a whole, for with small numbers, the influence of chance will obviously be considerable. In such circumstances we apply the theory of error, and calculate a quantity known as the *Standard Error*. This indicates the probability that a given result will be equalled or surpassed by luck. Statistical significance is regarded as being attained when a quantity equals twice its standard error, that is to say, when the odds are roughly 20 : 1 against the result being due to chance alone. The reason for taking 2 × the Standard Error (S.E.) as the level *which begins to suggest* significance is this.

The chance of exceeding S.E. ×1 by luck is 1 in 3
　　,,　　,,　　,,　　S.E. ×2 ,,　,,　,, 1 in 22
　　　　　　　　　　　but
The chance of exceeding S.E. ×3 by luck is 1 in 370
　　,,　　,,　　,,　　S.E. ×4 ,,　,,　,, 1 in 17,000.

Consequently S.E. ×2 stands, as it were, about the place where the descent becomes very steep, so that a slight excess only over it makes the probability of attaining the result by luck quite small.

The standard error of a percentage is given by the formula:

$$\sqrt{[p(100-p)/n]},$$

[1] A summary of some of the most useful statistical procedures will be found in my *Practical Animal Ecology* (Chs. 4 and 5).

where p is the percentage and n is the total number. Some examples will show how this can be used in practice.

(1) Suppose we are collecting the Freshwater Shrimp (*Gammarus pulex*) in a stream where a proportion of these are known to be parasitized by the protozoan *Dendrocometes*. What percentage is infected? We cannot capture all the *Gammarus*, and we therefore examine a *sample* of them, say, 200. Ten of *our sample* (5 per cent) are found with parasites. How does the sample reflect the situation in the population from which it was withdrawn? To answer this question we determine the standard error of the sample, which is calculated as:

$$\sqrt{[(5 \times 95)/200]} = 1 \cdot 6.$$

We therefore now write the result as $5 \pm 1 \cdot 6$ per cent. That is to say, the chances are approximately 20 : 1 that the true proportion of infected individuals *in the population as a whole* lies within the range $5 \pm 3 \cdot 2$ per cent.

(2) A similar procedure can be used if we have grounds for *expecting* a certain result, and we wish to know the extent to which the conditions in a sample conform with expectation. For instance, suppose we find in our sample of 200 *Gammarus* that 55 per cent are males, and we wish to determine whether this can be regarded as a significant departure from sex equality. In this instance we have an *expected ratio* and must therefore use it as the basis for calculating the standard error, i.e.:

$$\sqrt{(50 \times 50/200)} = 3 \cdot 54.$$

The divergence from expectation in the sample is 5, and since this is less than twice the standard error we can conclude that a sample of the size used does not demonstrate a significant departure from a 50 per cent ratio.

Percentages, like any other standards, have little meaning alone; the ecologist constantly needs to *compare* them. A general formula exists for the standard error of the *difference* between any two quantities whose standard errors are known, whether these be percentages or any other statistics.

Suppose A is the standard error of one quantity and B that of another comparable one. The standard error of the difference is given by the expression:

$$\sqrt{(A^2+B^2)}.$$

Let us illustrate this by means of a further example. In a backwater of the same stream in which the previous *Gammarus pulex* collection had been made, it is found that more of the individuals are females, presumably sheltering there on account of their larger size. The proportion of males in a sample of 150 is only 40 per cent. Is the difference between the two samples a 'real' one in the sense that it indicates a distinct ecological habitat influencing the occurrence of the two sexes, or is it due merely to luck? The standard errors of the two samples are 3·52 and 4 respectively. We thus express their difference as:

$$55-40=15\pm\sqrt{(3\cdot52^2+4^2)}=15\pm5\cdot33.$$

Thus the difference, being nearly 3 times the standard error, is 'significant' and indicates that the conditions of the stream in these two places have a genuine influence upon the distribution of the sexes which inhabit them.

In the field, it is often useful to be able to apply a quick check to see if two figures depart significantly from an expected *equality*. For instance, this may prove a valuable guide when deciding on the number of individuals to collect in order to obtain a significant result. An approximate test can be made as follows: subtract 1 from the difference between the two numbers; square the result, and divide this by their sum. Significance is achieved when the resulting figure is greater than 4. This can be represented as:

$$\frac{(D-1)^2}{N}>4 \text{ (for significance)},$$

where D is the difference between the two numbers and N is their sum. The method provides a fair guide, but when analysing results the standard error should be calculated as already described.

No attempt will be made here to explain the mathematical basis for tests of significance, nor does space permit consideration of the far more sensitive χ^2 test, which should always be used when grouped data are to be compared with expected values as, for instance, in Mendelian ratios. For further information on this important aspect of ecology, reference should be made to the various works included in the Bibliography. Special attention should be paid to the fact that the χ^2 distribution can be used to test the heterogeneity of such data, so that it is possible to determine whether or not a number of separate samples can be safely pooled to provide a sufficient total.

ESTIMATION OF THE TOTAL POPULATION

In certain circumstances an estimate of the total population can be obtained by the sampling methods already described. Suppose we are dealing with a colony of butterflies or water beetles, and we catch 50 and mark them so that they can be easily identified if recaught. These should be released, and allowed to assort themselves within the population once more. If in a further sample of 50, 5 are found to be marked, we can calculate the population as $\dfrac{50 \times 50}{5} = 500$. Such a simple procedure can only be employed with animals which randomize quickly once they are released, and are easily marked without damage. Quickly-drying cellulose paint will be found particularly suitable for this purpose. It can now be obtained in a variety of colours, and these can be used to denote the different samples if a series of continuous observations is being made. In this connection, it is important to realize that the method takes no account of increases or decreases in the population between one sample and the next, due to such causes as emergence and deaths. When estimating numbers over a period of time, allowance for such changes are, of course, made. The fact that this is possible enables one to compare such factors as death-rate in different forms, and so to detect the operation of Natural Selection. The procedure involved has been fully discussed elsewhere, and for further details the appropriate literature should be consulted.[1]

CONCLUSION

In the preceding chapters I have attempted to survey briefly some of the main aspects of this vast and ever expanding subject of Animal Ecology. Much has inevitably been omitted, and it is to be hoped that the references for further reading included in the Bibliography may make good this deficiency to some extent. In particular, the preceding chapter on Practical Ecology has been compressed to its smallest limits.

If, however, this book has succeeded in stimulating interest in the subject, and in encouraging the student to carry out small ecological investigations for himself, it will have achieved its object. For there is no better medium than practical ecology for developing initiative and an appreciation of scientific method. Furthermore, an array of unsolved problems is presented even at an elementary stage; many of them can be attacked successfully with even the simplest equipment, in striking contrast to the situation encountered in the majority of sciences. Here then are golden opportunities for anyone with some originality to undertake a piece of research which actually advances knowledge; surely a stimulus calculated to turn a student into an enthusiast.

---

[1] Fisher, R. A. and Ford, E. B. (1947) *Heredity*, 1, 143–74.
Dowdeswell, W. H., Fisher R. A. and Ford, E. B. (1940) *Annals of Eugenics*, x, 123–36.
Dowdeswell, W. H., Fisher R. A., and Ford, E. B. (1949) *Heredity*, III, 67–84.
Dowdeswell, W. H. (1959), *Practical Animal Ecology*; Methuen.

ABBREVIATED ANIMAL CLASSIFICATION

Phylum   PROTOZOA, e.g. *Chlamydomonas; Amoeba; Paramecium; Monocystis.*

Phylum   PORIFERA (Sponges), e.g. *Desmacidon.*
Branch   *DIPLOBLASTICA.*

Phylum   COELENTERATA.
Class   Hydrozoa,
              e.g. *Obelia; Hydra; Velella.*
Class   Scyphomedusae (Jelly fishes).
              e.g. *Aurelia.*
Class   Anthozoa (Sea anemones, corals, etc.).
              e.g. *Alcyonium; Actinia; Caryophyllia.*

Phylum   CTENOPHORA,
              e.g. *Pleurobrachia.*
Branch   *TRIPLOBLASTICA.*

Phylum   PLATYHELMINTHES (Flatworms).
Class   Turbellaria (Free-living forms).
              e.g. *Dendrocoelum; Polycelis.*
Class   Trematoda (Flukes).
              e.g. *Fasciola; Polystomum.*
Class   Cestoda (Tapeworms).
              e.g. *Taenia; Dipylidium.*

Phylum   NEMERTINA (Ribbon worms).
              e.g. *Lineus.*

Phylum   NEMATODA (Roundworms).
              e.g. *Ascaris; Ankylostoma.*

Phylum   ANNELIDA (Segmented worms)
Class   Polychaeta (Bristle worms).
              e.g. *Nereis; Arenicola.*
Class   Oligochaeta.
              e.g. *Tubifex; Lumbricus.*
Class   Archiannelida.
              e.g. *Polygordius; Protodrilus.*

Class   Hirudinea (Leeches).
                 e.g. *Hirudo; Glossosiphonia.*
Class   Gephyrea.
                 e.g. *Sipunculus; Phascolosoma.*

Phylum   ROTIFERA (Wheel Animalcules).
                 e.g. *Notops.*

Phylum   ARTHROPODA.
Class   Crustacea (Crabs, lobsters, shrimps, water-fleas,
                 wood-lice, etc.).
Class   Insecta (Insects).
Class   Arachnida (Scorpions, king crabs, spiders, ticks,
                 mites).
Class   Myriapoda (Centipedes, millipedes).
                 e.g. *Lithobius; Iulus.*

Phylum   MOLLUSCA.
Class   Amphineura.
                 e.g. *Chiton.*
Class   Gastropoda.
                 e.g. *Patella; Littorina; Limnaea; Helix.*
Class   Lamellibranchia (Bivalves).
                 e.g. *Mytilus; Anodonta; Teredo.*
Class   Cephalopoda (Squids, cuttlefishes, octopuses, etc.).
                 e.g. *Sepia; Loligo; Eledone.*

Phylum   BRACHIOPODA (Lamp shells).
                 e.g. *Lingula; Crania.*

Phylum   ECHINODERMATA.
Class   Asteroidea (Starfishes).
                 e.g. *Asterias; Marthasterias.*
Class   Ophiuroidea (Brittle Stars).
                 e.g. *Ophiothrix; Ophiocomina.*
Class   Echinoidea (Sea Urchins).
                 e.g. *Echinus; Psammechinus.*
Class   Holothuroidea (Sea Cucumbers).
                 e.g. *Holothuria; Cucumaria.*
Class   Crinoidea (Sea Lilies).
                 e.g. *Antedon.*

Phylum	CHORDATA.
Sub-phylum	Hemichordata.
Class	Pterobranchia.
	e.g. *Cephalodiscus*.
Class	Enteropneusta.
	e.g. *Balanoglossus*.
Sub-phylum	Protochordata (Acrania).
Class	Urochordata.
	e.g. *Ascidia; Salpa; Fritillaria; Oikopleura*.
Class	Cephalochordata.
	e.g. *Amphioxus*.
Sub-phylum	Craniata.
Class	Cyclostomata.
	e.g. *Lampetra; Petromyzon; Myxine*.
Class	Pisces (Fishes).
Sub-class	Chondrichthyes (Cartilaginous fishes).
Sub-class	Osteichthyes (Bony fishes).
Class	Amphibia (Frogs, newts, etc.).
Class	Reptilia (Snakes, lizards, etc.).
Class	Aves (Birds).
Class	Mammalia (Mammals).
Sub-class	Monotremata.
	e.g. *Echidna; Ornithorhynchus*.
Sub-class	Ditremata
Grade	Marsupialia (Marsupials).
Grade	Placentalia (Placentals).

GLOSSARY

Acheulian culture. That belonging to men living in the earlier part of the Old Stone (Palaeolithic) Age and of a different species from ours.

Allelomorphs (Alleles). A pair of genes situated in identical positions on homologous chromosomes, and controlling the same character or set of characters.

Aposematic colours. Those which advertise the presence of an organism to potential predators to denote the inadvisability of attack.

Atlantic climate. Wet with mild winters and summers rather warmer than to-day. About 5000–2500 B.C.

Aurignacian culture. That of *Homo sapiens* living in caves. It immediately followed the Mousterian, and belongs to the later part of the Old Stone Age.

Autecology. The ecological relationships of a particular animal or plant species.

Average density. The number of animals per unit area in a locality, irrespective of whether the whole of that locality has been colonized or not (see *Economic density*).

Barrier. Any ecological factor which restricts the increase in range of a species.

Batesian mimicry. The resemblance of a palatable to a distasteful species for protective purposes.

Biotic factors. Biological factors resulting from the interaction of living organisms with one another, such as food, living space, etc.

Boreal climate. Dry, with warm summers and cold winters. About 6800–5000 B.C.

Carotin. An orange-coloured pigment related to chlorophyll produced only by plants.

Caste. A group of social insects which have become specialized to perform a particular function.

Chellean culture. The earliest known human culture.

Climatic factors. Biological factors which are mainly physical in nature such as temperature, light, and moisture.

Cline. A graded series of changes in an organism, either structural or physiological, taking place gradually within a particular zone.

Commensalism. The situation arising when two animals (*commensals*) belonging to different species, live together without becoming physiologically interdependent. The advantages may be one-sided or mutual.

Cretaceous period. The latest period of the Mesozoic era lasting about 48 million years. It includes the chalk.

Cryptic colours. Those which tend to match the surroundings in which an animal lives.

Degeneration. The loss or reduction of certain organs. This is correlated with the animal's mode of life.

Density. The number of animals per unit area.

Detritus. Small particles of organic matter occurring in aquatic habitats which result from the decay of dead animals and plants.

Dimorphism. The occurrence together of two forms of the same species.

Dominant. A character as fully developed when the genes determining it are heterozygous as when they are homozygous (see *Recessive*).

Ecological niche. An economic status occupied by an animal within a community, resulting from its adaptation to a particular set of environmental conditions, particularly food supply.

Ecology. The relationships of living organisms with one another and their environment.

Economic density. The number of animals per unit area in localities which have been colonized (see *Average density*).

Ectoparasite. A parasite living on the exterior of its host.

Endoparasite. A parasite which lives inside the body of its host.

Environment. The sum total of the conditions in which an organism lives.

Environmental variation. Variation in a character of an organism due to external influences and occurring irrespective of any alteration in its hereditary constitution (see *Genetic variation*).

Epigamic colours. Those occurring in animals for the purpose of courtship and display to the opposite sex.

Epizoite. An animal which occurs on the exterior of another living animal (the host) from which it may derive protection. Epizoites are generally also able to lead an independent existence.

Erythrocruorin. A respiratory pigment similar to haemoglobin found in various invertebrates.

Euryhaline. Able to tolerate a wide range of external osmotic changes.

Eurythermous. Able to tolerate a wide range of temperature variation.

Facultative parasite. A parasite which is also capable of leading a free-living existence.

Food chain. A complex relationship between the different animals of a community in respect of their food requirements. All chains invariably terminate in plants on which animals are ultimately dependent.

Galvanometer. An instrument for detecting the flow of an electric current.

Gene complex. The sum total of the genetic factors of an organism interacting to produce an internal environment in which all the genes must operate.

Genes. The hereditary units. They are responsible for the production of a given set of characters in any particular environment.

Genetics. The study of heredity and variation.

Genetic variation. Variation in a character of an organism occurring as a result of mutation or recombination of genes.

Genotype. An animal judged by its genetic constitution (see *Phenotype*).

Geology. The study of the history, development, and structure of the earth's crust.

Hermaphrodite. A single organism possessing both male and female reproductive organs.

Heterozygous. An individual in which the members of a given pair of genes (allelomorphs) are dissimilar.

Highest density. The maximum number of animals able to occupy a unit area of habitat.

Holocene period. Recent geological times since the last Ice Age.

Homiothermous. Having a body temperature which is constant and independent of that of the environment (i.e. birds and mammals).

Homozygous. An individual in which the members of a given pair of genes (allelomorphs) are similar.

Host. A living organism at whose expense a parasite exists or on which an epizoite lives.

Hydrotaxis. The movement of an animal towards (positive) or away from (negative) a source of water.

Hyperparasite. An animal parasitizing another which is itself a parasite.

Hypertonic. Having a higher osmotic pressure.

Hypotonic. Having a lower osmotic pressure.

Igneous rocks. Those whose formation has resulted from volcanic action.

Indigenous animal. One regarded as a native of a particular locality.

Isotonic. Having the same osmotic pressure.

Jurassic period. A period of about 25 million years' duration which ended about 100 million years ago, during which time reptiles were the predominant animals.

Larva. A young stage of an animal whose change to an adult involves complete metamorphosis (see *Nymph*).

Littorine animals. Those inhabiting the region of the shore.

Lowest density. The minimum number of animals able to exist in a unit area of habitat.

Magdalenian culture. The last of the Old Stone (Palaeolithic) Age cultures.

Melanic form. An animal whose colour is brown or black on account of the presence of the pigment melanin.

Melanin. A nitrogenous animal pigment with a black or brownish colour.

Mesozoic era. An era of about 125 million years' duration which ended about 50 million years ago. The age of amphibians and reptiles.

Metamorphosis. A change from the young to the adult stage in an animal involving both external and internal reorganization of tissues.

Migration. The movement of animals often in mass, from one locality to another for the purpose of breeding.

Mousterian culture. That immediately following the Acheulian culture, and belonging to the middle part of the Old Stone (Palaeolithic) Age.

Müllerian mimicry. The convergence in evolution of two or more well protected aposematic species to assume a similar appearance.

Multiple indicator. An indicator whose colour varies with different concentrations of hydrogen ions.

Mutation. The inception of a heritable variation.

Nymph. A young stage of an animal in which the change to an adult involves only partial (incomplete) metamorphosis (see *Larva*).

Optimum density. The density of an animal population best suited to its existence in a particular habitat.

Optimum density range. The range of density within which an animal community is able to fluctuate without becoming subject to the ill effects of either overcrowding or undercrowding.

Osmo-regulation. The process of regulating osmotic pressure.

Palaeontology. The study of extinct animals and plants from evidence provided by geological strata.

Palaeozoic era. The earliest era of which we have detailed knowledge. It lasted about 325 million years and ended approximately 175 million years ago.

Parasite. An organism which lives either partially or completely at the expense of another living animal or plant (the host).

Parasite chain. The food relationships existing between different parasites and their hosts.

Parasitoids. Organisms possessing alternating parasitic and free-living phases.

Parthenogenesis. The development of an egg without fertilization.

Passerine bird. Belonging to the Order Passeriformes, a large group of birds which have become specialized for perching and singing. All have feet with three toes in front and one behind.

Phenotype. An animal judged by its appearance (see *Genotype*).

Photosynthesis. A process occurring in green plants whereby sugar is formed in the presence of sunlight, a by-product being oxygen.

Phototaxis. The movement of an animal towards (positive) or away from (negative) a source of light.

Phototropism. The bending of a static organism towards (positive) or away from (negative) a source of light.

Physiographic factors. Ecological influences resulting from the nature of the surroundings.

Physiology. The study of the various vital processes occurring in living organisms.

Plankton. Minute drifting aquatic plants and animals whose distribution is largely determined by the current.

Plant succession. A series of changes in the flora of a locality, due to such factors as soil composition and illumination, generally resulting directly from the influence of the plants themselves.

Pleistocene period. The period of the great ice ages previous to recent (Holocene) times.

Pliocene period. The geological period immediately preceding the Pleistocene, of about $9\frac{1}{2}$ million years' duration.

Poikilothermous. Cold blooded, i.e. a condition in which the body temperature of an animal is dependent on that of the environment.

Polymorphism. The occurrence together of two or more forms of the same species.

Post Office Box. An apparatus containing a number of electrical resistances of known value.

Pre-boreal climate. Dry and cold. About 8300–6800 B.C.

Predator. An animal which preys upon other living animals.

Profile chart. A method of representing graphically the distribution of plants and animals along a particular line, from a vertical point of view.

Pyramid of numbers. A figurative method of representing the relationship of size to density in an animal community.

Quadrat. A square of known size, used to determine the distribution and density of plants in different localities.

Recessive. A character produced only when the genes controlling it are homozygous (see *Dominant*).

Relict fauna. A remnant of a previous fauna: e.g. Glacial relict (one left behind by the retreating ice at the end of the Pleistocene period).

Rheotaxis. A response by an animal to the stimulus of the impact of a water current. Positive rheotaxy denotes a tendency to move against the current, negative rheotaxy, movement with it.

Significance (statistical). A measure of the reliability of a difference between observation and expectation.

Specialization. Structural or physiological adaptation by an organism to a particular set of environmental conditions.

Specificity. The dependence of an organism for its existence on a close physiological relationship with another particular species of animal.

Specific modifier. A gene modifying the characters produced by other genes. It may be without effect by itself.

Standard error. A quantity calculated to show the probability that a given result will be equalled or surpassed by chance.

Stenohaline. Able to tolerate only a narrow range of external osmotic changes.

Stenothermous. Able to withstand only small variations in temperature.

Stratified rocks. Those which have been deposited in water and laid down upon the earth's surface in successive layers (strata).

Sub-Atlantic climate. That characteristic of Britain to-day. Dated from about 1000 B.C.

Symbiosis. The situation when two organisms (symbionts) exist together in close physiological union without normally becoming parasitic on one another. The advantages conferred are generally mutual.

Synecology. The ecological relationships of any group of organisms forming a community.

Taxonomy. The process of description, classification, and naming of animals and plants.

Thermistor. A capsule containing a complex metal oxide whose resistance decreases rapidly with increasing temperature.

Thermotaxis. The movement of an animal towards (positive) or away from (negative) a source of heat.

Transect. A method of representing graphically the distribution of animals and plants from a horizontal point of view.

Trophallaxis. A process of mutual feeding which occurs among some social insects.

Tundra. Conditions in which the subsoil remains permanently frozen while the surface thaws in summer only.

Vector (*Secondary host*). An animal other than the host which acts as a means of transmission and dispersal of a parasite. The life-cycle of the parasite is continued in a secondary host but not in a vector.

Viviparous animal. One in which the embryo develops within the body of the mother.

BIBLIOGRAPHY

ANIMAL AND PLANT ECOLOGY

Allee, W. C., Emerson, A. E., Park, T., and Schmidt, K. P. (1949), *A Fundamental Treatise on Ecology*; Saunders. (Standard American work of reference.)

Carpenter, K. E. (1928), *Life in Inland Waters*; Sidgwick and Jackson.

Chapman, R. N. (1931), *Animal Ecology*; McGraw-Hill.

Dowdeswell, W. H. (1959), *Practical Animal Ecology*; Methuen.

Elton, C. (1953, 3rd edn.), *The Ecology of Animals*; Methuen.

Elton, C. (1958), *The Ecology of Invasions by Animals and Plants*; Methuen.

Ennion, E. A. R. (1946), *Life on the Sea Shore*; Oxford.

Greig-Smith, P. (1957), *Quantitative Plant Ecology*; Butterworth.

Hepburn, I. (1952), *Flowers of the Coast*; Collins.

Leach, W. (1957, 4th edn.), *Plant Ecology*; Methuen.

Lousley, J. E. (1950), *Wild Flowers of Chalk and Limestone*; Collins.

Macan, T. T., and Worthington, E. B. (1951), *Life in Lakes and Rivers*; Collins.

Macfadyen, A. (1957), *Animal Ecology*; Pitman.

McLean, R. C., and Cook, W. R. I. (1943), *Practical Field Ecology*; Allen and Unwin.

Odum, E. P. (1954), *Fundamentals of Ecology*; Saunders.

Pearsall, W. H. (1950), *Mountains and Moorlands*; Collins.

Raven, J., and Walters, M. (1956), *Mountain Flowers*; Collins.

Salisbury, E. (1952), *Downs and Dunes*; Bell.

Sankey, J. (1958), *A Guide to Field Biology*; Longmans. (Excellent elementary introduction.)

Tansley, A. G. (1949), *Britain's Green Mantle*; Allen and Unwin.

Tansley, A. G. (1946), *Introduction to Plant Ecology*; Allen and Unwin.

Tansley, A. G. (1939), *The British Islands and their Vegetation*; Cambridge (standard work of reference).

Tansley, A. G., and Price Evans, E. (1947), *Plant Ecology for the School*; Allen and Unwin. (Good elementary account.)

Turrill, W. B. (1948), *British Plant Life*; Collins.

Wilson, D. P. (1951, 2nd edn.), *Life of the Shore and Shallow Sea*; Nicolson and Watson.

Yonge, C. M. (1949), *The Sea Shore*; Collins.

COLORATION AND MIMICRY

Brown, E. S. (1951), *Mimicry as illustrated in the British Fauna (New Biology No. 10)*; Penguin.

Carpenter, G. D. H., and Ford, E. B. (1933), *Mimicry*; Methuen.

Cott, H. B. (1940), *Adaptive Coloration in Animals*; Methuen.

Parker, G. H. (1948), *Animal Colour Changes*; Cambridge.

Stephenson, E. M. (1946), *Animal Camouflage*; Pelican.

Wilson, D. P. (1951, 2nd edn.), *Life of the Shore and Shallow Sea*; Nicholson and Watson.

ECONOMIC AND APPLIED ECOLOGY

British Museum (Natural History), *Economic Series* of monographs dealing with specific animals.

Burr, M. (1954, 2nd edn.), *The Insect Legion*; Nisbet.

Edlin, H. L. (1956), *Trees, Woods and Man*; Collins.

Elton, C. (1958), *The Ecology of Invasions by Plants and Animals*; Methuen.

Good, R. (1933), *Plants and Human Economics*; Cambridge.

Graham, M. (1949, 2nd edn.), *The Fish Gate*; Faber and Faber.

Hill, A. F. (1937), *Economic Botany*; McGraw-Hill.

Lancum, F. H. (1948), *Wild Birds and the Land*; H.M. Stationery Office.

Lancum, F. H. (1951), *Wild Mammals and the Land*; H.M. Stationery Office.

Nicol, H. (1943), *The Biological Control of Insects*; Pelican.

Russell, E. S. (1942), *The Overfishing Problem*; Cambridge.

Schery, R. W. (1954), *Plants for Man*; Allen and Unwin.

Stamp, L. D. (1955), *Man and the Land*; Collins.

Thompson, H. V., and Worden, A. N. (1956), *The Rabbit*; Collins.

Wardle, R. A. (1929), *The Principles of Applied Zoology*; Longmans.

Wardle, R. A. (1929), *The Problems of Applied Entomology*; Manchester University Press.

GENETICS AND EVOLUTION

Auerbach, C. (1956), *Genetics in the Atomic Age*; Oliver and Boyd.

Cain, A. J. (1945), *Animal Species and their Evolution*; Hutchinson's University Library.

Darlington, C. D. (1956), *Chromosome Botany*; Allen and Unwin.

Darlington, C. D. and Mather K. (1950), *Genes, Plants, and People*; Allen and Unwin.

Darlington, C. D., and Mather, K. (1949), *The Elements of Genetics*; Allen and Unwin.

Darwin, C. (1859, reprinted 1929), *The Origin of Species*; Oxford.

Dobzhansky, T. (1951, 3rd edn.), *Genetics and the Origin of Species*; Columbia.

Dowdeswell, W. H. (1958, 2nd edn.), *The Mechanism of Evolution*; Heinemann.

Ford, E. B. (1949, 5th edn.), *Mendelism and Evolution*; Methuen.

Ford, E. B. (1949, 2nd edn.), *The Study of Heredity*; Home University Library.

Huxley, J. (1945, 5th edn.), *Evolution. The Modern Synthesis*; Allen and Unwin.

Lack, D. (1947), *Darwin's Finches*; Cambridge.

Mayr, E. (1942), *Systematics and the Origin of Species*; Columbia.

Sheppard, P. M. (1958), *Natural Selection and Heredity*; Hutchinson.

Simpson, G. G. (1950), *The Meaning of Evolution*; Oxford.

Srb, A. M., and Owen, R. D. (1957), *General Genetics*; Freeman, California.

Waddington, C. H. (1939), *An Introduction to Modern Genetics*; Allen and Unwin.

GEOLOGY AND PALAEONTOLOGY

Gilluly, J., Waters, A. C., and Woodford, A. O. (1958), *Principles of Geology*; Freeman.

Holmes, A. (1944), *Principles of Physical Geology*; Nelson.

Smith, B. W. (1947, 4th edn.), *The World in the Past*; Warne.

Swinnerton, H. H. (1958), *The Earth Beneath Us;* Pelican.

Wells, A. K. (1959, 4th edn.), *Outline of Historical Geology*; Murby.

IDENTIFICATION OF ANIMALS

Animals (General)

Barrett, J., and Yonge, C. M. (1958), *Pocket Guide to the Sea Shore*; Collins. (Excellent for identification of animals and plants.)

Smart, J., and Taylor, G. (1955), *Bibliography of Key Works for the Identification of the British Fauna and Flora*. The Systematics Association (c/o British Museum (Nat. Hist.)). (An excellent and cheap comprehensive summary.)

(a) VERTEBRATES

Amphibians

Sandars, E. (1937), *A Beast Book for the Pocket*; Oxford.

Smith, M. (1949), *British Reptiles and Amphibia*; King Penguin.

Smith, M. (1951), *The British Amphibians and Reptiles*; Collins.

Birds

Fisher, J. (1951), *Bird Recognition* (2 vols.); Pelican.

Fitter, R. S. R. (1954), *The Pocket Guide to British Birds*; Collins. (Good for beginners.)

Gibson-Hill, C. A. (1947), *British Sea Birds*; Witherby.

Peterson, R., Mountfort, G., and Hollom, P. A. D. (1954), *A Field Guide to the Birds of Britain and Europe*; Collins. (Outstanding for field identification; beautifully illustrated.)

Witherby, H. F., Jourdain, F. C. R., Ticehurst, N. F., and Tucker, B. W. (1947, 4th edn.), *Handbook of British Birds* (5 vols.); Witherby. (Standard work of reference.)

Fishes

Hodgson, N. B., (1948), *Freshwater Fishes of the British Isles*; Crowther.

Jenkins, J. T. (1956, 2nd edn.), *The Fishes of the British Isles*; Warne.

Mammals

Hodgson, N. B. (1945), *Mammals and Reptiles of the British Isles*; Crowther.

Matthews, L. H. (1952), *British Mammals*; Collins.

Sandars, E. (1937), *A Beast Book for the Pocket*; Oxford.

Reptiles

Hodgson, N. B. (1945), *Mammals and Reptiles of the British Isles*; Crowther.

Sandars, E. (1937), *A Beast Book for the Pocket*; Oxford.

Smith, M. (1949), *British Reptiles and Amphibia*; King Penguin.

Smith, M. (1951), *The British Amphibians and Reptiles*; Collins.

(b) INVERTEBRATES

General

Eales, N. B. (1950, 2nd edn.), *The Littoral Fauna of Great Britain*; Cambridge.

Kevan, D. K. McE. (editor) (1955), *Soil Zoology*; Butterworth. (Excellent elementary key to soil fauna included as an Appendix).

Mellanby, H. (1953, 5th edn.), *Animal Life in Fresh Water*; Methuen.
For detailed treatment of the various groups of aquatic inverte-brates, see the excellent series of pamphlets on identification pub-lished by The Freshwater Biological Association, Windermere.

Annelids
Černosvitov, L., and Evans, A. C. (1947), *Lumbricidae, No. 6 of Synopses of the British Fauna*; Linnean Society (London).

Arthropods
(*a*) *Arachnids*
Baker, E. W., and Wharton, G. W. (1952), *An Introduction to Acarology*; Macmillan.
Bristowe, W. S. (1947), *Spiders*; King Penguin.
Bristowe, W. S. (1958), *The World of Spiders*; Collins.
Cloudsley-Thompson, J. L. (1958), *Spiders, Scorpions, Centipedes and Mites*; Pergamon Press.
Locket, G. H., and Millidge, A. F. (1951–3), *British Spiders* (2 vols.); Ray Society, London.
Savory, T. H. (1945, 2nd edn.), *The Spiders and Allied Orders of the British Isles*; Warne.

(*b*) *Crustaceans*
Edney, E. B. (1954), *British Woodlice, No. 9 of Synopses of the British Fauna*. Linnean Society (London).
Ward, H. B., and Whipple, G. C. (1918), *Freshwater Biology*; London. (Good for some of the smaller forms. American species only. See also references under *General*.)

(*c*) *Insects*
For detailed treatment of the various Orders see the separate parts of the *Handbook for the Identification of British Insects*. Royal Entomological Society, London.
Burr, M. (1936), *British Grasshoppers and their Allies*; Philip Allen.
Chrystal, R. N. (1937), *Insects of the British Woodlands*; Warne.
Colyer, C. N., and Hammond, C. O. (1951), *Flies of the British Isles*; Warne.
Dibb, J. R. (1948), *Field Book of Beetles*; Hull.
Donisthorpe, H. St. K. (1927), *British Ants*; Routledge.
Ford, E. B. (1946, 2nd edn.), *Butterflies*; Collins.

Ford, E. B. (1955), *Moths*; Collins.

Hickin, N. E. (1952), *Caddis*; Methuen.

Imms, A. D. (1957), *A General Textbook of Entomology*; Methuen.

Imms, A. D. (1947), *Insect Natural History*; Collins.

Joy, N. H. (1932), *A Practical Handbook of British Beetles*; Witherby.

Joy, N. H. (1944), *British Beetles. Their Homes and Habits*; Warne.

Kloet, G. S., and Hincks, W. D. (1945). *A Check List of the British Insects*; Stockport. (An invaluable check-list, generally regarded as the standard work.)

Longfield, C. (1937), *Dragonflies of the British Isles*; Warne.

Marshall, J. F. (1938), *The British Mosquitoes*; British Museum (Nat. Hist.).

Morley, D. W. (1955), *Ants*; Collins.

Pickard, B. C. (1954), *Grasshoppers and Crickets of Great Britain*. (Private publication.)

Sandars, E. (1946), *An Insect Book for the Pocket*; Oxford.

South, R. (1943, 3rd edn.), *The Butterflies of the British Isles*; Warne.

South, R. (1943, 3rd edn.), *The Moths of the British Isles*; Warne.

Step, E. (1932), *Bees, Wasps, Ants and Allied Insects of the British Isles*; Warne.

Stokoe, W. J. (1944), *The Caterpillars of the British Butterflies*; Warne.

Stokoe, W. J. (1948), *The Caterpillars of the British Moths* (2 vols.); Warne.

Myriapods

Blower, G. (1952), *British Millipedes with Special Reference to Yorkshire Species*; *The Naturalist*, London.

Molluscs

Ellis, A. E. (1928), *British Snails*; Oxford.

Quick, H. E. (1949), '*Testicellidae, Arionidae, Limacidae*' (Slugs), *No. 8 of Synopses of the British Fauna*. Linnean Society (London).

Step, E. (1945), *Shell Life*; Warne.

Nematodes

Goodey, T. (1951), *Soil and Freshwater Nematodes*; Methuen.

Protozoans

Sandon, H. (1927), *The Composition and Distribution of the Protozoan Fauna of the Soil*; Oliver and Boyd.

IDENTIFICATION OF PLANTS

Clapham, A. R., Tutin, T. G., and Warburg, E. F. (1952), *Flora of the British Isles*; Cambridge. (Standard British Work.)

Gilmour, J., and Walters, M. (1954), *Wild Flowers*; Collins.

Hutchinson, J. (1955, 2nd edn.), *British Wild Flowers* (2 vols.); Pelican.

Makins, F. K. (1957, 2nd edn.), *Concise Flora of Britain*; Oxford.

McClintock, D., and Fitter, R. S. R. (1956), *The Pocket Guide to Wild Flowers*; Collins. (Excellent elementary book, well illustrated, mostly in colour.)

Newton, L. (1951), *Handbook of the British Seaweeds*; British Museum (Nat. Hist.), London.

Prime, C. T., and Deacock, R. J. (1953, 2nd edn.), *A Shorter British Flora*; Methuen.

Skene, N. (1952, 2nd edn.), *A Flower Book for the Pocket*; Oxford. (Good for beginners, illustrated in colour.)

MIGRATION

Buxton, J. (1950), *The Redstart*; Collins.

Calderwood, W. L. (1931), *Salmon Hatching and Salmon Migrations*; Arnold.

Ennion, E. A. R. (1947), *The Story of Migration*; Harrap

Katz, D. (1953), *Animals and Men*; Pelican.

Lockley, R. M. (1942), *Shearwaters*; Dent.

Matthews, G. V. T. (1955), *Bird Navigation*; Cambridge.

Roule, L. (1933), *Fishes, their Journeys and Migrations*; Routledge and Kegan Paul.

Rowan, W. (1931), *The Riddle of Migration*; Baltimore.

Smith, S. (1950); *The Yellow Wagtail*; Collins.

Thomson, A. L. (1944, 2nd edn.), *Bird Migration*; Witherby.

Williams, C. B. (1958), *Insect Migration*; Collins.

NATURAL HISTORY (GENERAL)

Bates, H. W. (1895), *The Naturalist on the Amazons*. Murray.

Coward, T. A. (1945, 5th edn.), *Life of the Wayside and Woodland*; Warne.

Darling, Fraser F. (1945), *The Natural History of the Highlands and Islands*; Collins.

Darling, Fraser F. (1943), *Wild Life in Britain*; Collins.

Darwin, C. (1845), *A Naturalist's Voyage Round the World*; Murray.

Fitter, R. S. R. (1945), *London's Natural History*; Collins.

Fleure, H. J. (1951), *A Natural History of Man in Britain*; Collins.
Imms, A. D. (1947), *Insect Natural History*; Collins.
Neal, E. (1948), *The Badger*; Collins.
Nicholson, E. M. (1951), *Birds and Men*; Collins.
North, F. J., Campbell, B., and Scott, R. (1949), *Snowdonia*; Collins.
Pearsall, W. H. (1950), *Mountains and Moorlands*; Collins.
Pitt, F. (1938), *Wild Animals of Britain*; Batsford.
Pycraft, W. P. (1931), *The Standard Natural History*; Warne.
Step, E. (1948, 11th edn.), *Animal Life of the British Isles*; Warne.
Tansley, A. G. (1945), *Our Heritage of Wild Nature*; Cambridge.
Turner, W. J. (editor) (1946), *Nature in Britain*; Collins.
Vesey-Fitzgerald, B. (1946), *British Game*; Collins.
Wallace, A. R. (1880), *Island Life*; Macmillan.
White, G. (1875), *Natural History of Selborne*; Macmillan.

PHYSIOLOGICAL ASPECTS OF ANIMAL ECOLOGY (OSMO-REGULATION, ETC.)

Baldwin, E. (1949, 3rd edn.), *An Introduction to Comparative Biochemistry*; Cambridge.
Ramsay, J. A. (1952), *A Physiological Approach to the Lower Animals*; Cambridge.
Yapp, W. B. (1945, 3rd edn.), *Animal Physiology*; Oxford.

SOCIAL BEHAVIOUR IN INSECTS

Butler, C. (1954), *The World of the Honey Bee*; Collins.
Donisthorpe, H. St. J. K. (1927), *Guests of the British Ants*; Routledge.
Imms, A. D. (1947), *Insect Natural History*; Collins.
Imms, A. D. (1938, 2nd edn.), *Social Behaviour in Insects*; Methuen.
Richards, O. W. (1953), *The Social Insects*; Macdonald.
Tinbergen, N. (1953), *Social Behaviour in Animals*; Methuen.
Von Frisch, K. (1954), *The Dancing Bees*; Methuen.

SOIL

Bear, F. E. (editor) (1955), *Chemistry of Soil*; Chapman and Hall.
Clarke, G. R. (1941), *The Study of Soil in the Field*; Oxford.
Darwin, C. (1881), *The Formation of Vegetable Mould Through the Action of Worms, with Observation of their Habits*; Murray.
Hall, A. D. (1944, 3rd edn.), *The Feeding of Crops and Stock* (3 vols.); Murray.

Jacks, G. V. (1954), *Soil*; Nelson.

James, W. O. (1957), *Background to Gardening*; Allen and Unwin.

Kevan, D. K. McE. (editor) (1955), *Soil Zoology*; Butterworth. (Includes an excellent key to identification of soil fauna.)

Knowles, F., and Watkin, J. E. (1947, 2nd edn.), *A Practical Course in Agricultural Chemistry*; Macmillan.

Manley, G. (1952), *Climate and the British Scene*; Collins.

Millar, C. E. (1955), *Soil Fertility*; Wiley.

Robinson, G. W. (1949), *Soils, their Origin, Constitution and Classification*; Murby.

Russell, E. J. (1950, 2nd edn.), *Lessons on Soil*; Cambridge. (Elementary practical course.)

Russell, E. J. (1954, 8th edn.), *Soil Conditions and Plant Growth*; Longmans. (Standard work on the subject.)

Russell, E. J. (1957), *The World of the Soil*; Collins. (Outstanding modern account.)

Smith, A. M. (1952), *Manures and Fertilizers*; Nelson.

Waksman, S. A. (1952), *Soil Microbiology*; Chapman and Hall.

SPECIAL ANIMAL RELATIONSHIPS (COMMENSALS, PARASITES, AND SYMBIONTS)

Butler, C. G. (1954), *The World of the Honey Bee*; Collins.

Cameron, T. W. M. (1956), *Parasites and Parasitism*; Methuen. (Outstanding general account.)

Caullery, M. (1952), *Parasitism and Symbiosis*; Sidgwick and Jackson.

Chandler, A. C. (1945), *Introduction to Parasitology with special Reference to the Parasites of Man*; Chapman and Hall.

Keeble, F. (1910), *Plant Animals*; Cambridge. (An account of symbiosis in *Convoluta*.)

Lapage, G. (1937), *Nematodes Parasitic in Animals*; Methuen.

Lapage, G. (1951), *Parasitic Animals*; Cambridge.

Rothschild, M. and Clay, T. (1952), *Fleas, Flukes and Cuckoos*; Collins.

Wilson, D. P. (1951, 2nd edn.), *Life of the Shore and Shallow Sea*; Nicholson & Watson.

Yonge, C. M. (1949), *The Sea Shore*; Collins.

STATISTICAL ANALYSIS AND QUANTITATIVE METHODS

Brookes, B. C., and Dick, W. F. L. (1953, 2nd edn.), *An Introduction to Statistical Method*; Heinemann.

Fisher, R. A. (1954, 12th edn.), *Statistical Methods for Research Workers*; Oliver and Boyd.

Fisher, R. A. (1951, 6th edn.), *The Design of Experiments*; Oliver and Boyd.

Greig-Smith, P. (1957), *Quantitative Plant Ecology*; Butterworth.

Mather, K. (1951, 4th edn.), *Statistical Analysis in Biology*; Methuen.

Snedecor, G. W. (1950, 4th edn.), *Statistical Methods*; Iowa. (An excellent American text-book.)

TERRITORIAL BEHAVIOUR

Armstrong, E. A. (1955), *The Wren*; Collins.

Buxton, J. (1950), *The Redstart*; Collins.

Howard, H. E. (1948), *Territory in Bird Life*; Witherby. (Original classic reprinted.)

Lack, D. (1946, 2nd edn.), *The Life of the Robin*; Witherby. (Also in Pelican edition.)

Smith, J. (1945), *How to Study Birds*; Collins.

Smith, S. (1950), *The Yellow Wagtail*; Collins.

INDEX

Figures in italics refer to text illustrations; those in bold figures, to plates.